Unit 5
Fire

Energy and Thermochemistry

Teacher Guide
Preliminary Edition

Angelica M. Stacy, Principal Author

Development Team: Jan Coonrod and Jennifer Claesgens

Acknowledgments:
Living By Chemistry has been developed at the Lawrence Hall of Science, University of California, Berkeley. This material is based upon work supported by the National Science Foundation grant No. ESI-9730634. Any opinions, findings, and conclusions or recommendations expressed in this material are those of the authors and do not necessarily reflect the views of the National Science Foundation or the Regents of the University of California.

The authors would like to thank Karen Chang, Nicci Nunes, and Daniel Quach for contributions to the development of the Fire Unit. David R. Dudley contributed the sketches of materials interspersed throughout the unit.

Cover Photo Credits:
Lit Match: RF/Corbis
Stove with Pan: C Squared Studios/Photodisc Green/Getty Images
Robot: Andy Sotiriou/Photodisc Red/Getty Images
Batteries: RF/Corbis
Power Plant: Malcolm Fife/PictureQuest
Flames: Ryan McVay/Photodisc Green/Getty Images

Published by Key Curriculum Press
Key Curriculum Press
1150 65th Street
Emeryville, CA 94608
510-595-7000
editorial@keypress.com
www.keypress.com

Printed in the United States of America
10 9 8 7 6 5 4 3 2 10 09 08 07 06

ISBN-13: 978-1-55953-710-0
ISBN-10: 1-55953-710-8

Fire Unit – Contents

Introduction

Teaching and Learning with *Living By Chemistry*

Humans develop ways of understanding the world around them based on their experiences. Learning is a personal interpretation of experience, and each person has to assimilate new information into an existing framework of understanding – one that is quite individual. So, every lesson in the *Living By Chemistry* (*LBC*) curriculum begins by activating student's prior understanding of and knowledge about a subject. Students *can* accumulate facts and information, but true understanding comes when they actively make sense of the new information that you give them or tell them directly, restructuring their existing ideas to accommodate it.

Using this curriculum you'll rarely ask students to accept any piece of information on faith alone, as scientific fact. They'll look for patterns in evidence and examples, and you'll encourage them to think and to come to their own conclusions. You'll notice that nomenclature and formal definitions are frequently introduced *after* students have explored, scrutinized, and developed a concept. At first, you might find it difficult to restrain yourself from telling the students the "facts" – what chemists seem to "know" to be true. Nevertheless, it is important for your success and theirs that you simply guide the inquiry and avoid preempting it, allowing the lessons to unfold and students' native curiosity to motivate them. We hope you'll agree that engaging students in an ongoing mental process is more likely to lead to true understanding. It also reflects more authentically the mindset and practice of real scientists.

The *LBC* approach requires your students to be active thinkers. Some students who have been successful in school by getting information passively (through lecture or assigned reading) may be uncomfortable with the new *LBC* approach at first. They have a formula for success – absorb the information, accept it as fact, and repeat it back to the instructor – but perhaps they don't have an understanding of the concepts Their success as students may dip at first or they might have trouble getting used to the fact that "the rules have changed." Eventually these students will become attuned to the new approach and will welcome the new challenges and the opportunity to share their ideas. On the other hand, with the *LBC* curriculum you'll ask students to think, ask questions, and understand. Students who have experienced only mediocre or partial success may begin to excel. As they are challenged to become more active participants in the classroom, they'll be encouraged to share their ideas and theories. They'll find that "wrong" or offbeat answers are not only greeted favorably, but become useful fodder for discussion.

In the long run, we have found that both groups of students benefit more from this approach, both in chemistry class and in their daily lives. A deeper understanding, rather than just a surface knowledge of chemistry, provides a substantial foundation for learning down the road. Developing critical thinking and problem-solving skills benefits all students in all facets of their lives. Being able to support their answers with evidence and to advance their own reasoning are skills they will need for eventual success at the college level and in the job world. Students who use the *LBC* curriculum testify that they are learning thinking and problem solving skills that they can apply in other classes and disciplines.

For ultimate success with this curriculum, your patience with the learning process and your trust in it will be indispensable. At first, this approach may seem to take a bit more time and may seem to start a little slower. In actuality students are probably learning more in less time. For instance, you may be skeptical that the students will indeed discover the appropriate patterns in structural formulas, which chemists refer to as functional groups. How much easier it seems to just point them out rather than take the time to let the students deduce them! Nevertheless, our experience shows, and field-test teachers confirm, that students not only *can* do these things, but that they retain and comprehend more as a result of having gone through the process. The scaffolding approach to learning, in which you guide students from what they know already to what you want them to learn, allows them to function at the cutting edge of their development.

Living By Chemistry begins with the basics. We don't assume that your students come into your classroom with any exposure to chemistry or its concepts. At first glance, introducing rudimentary concepts may seem detrimental to a student who has had some background in chemistry. Nevertheless, the *LBC* approach is different enough that a student with prior knowledge is actually learning new things in new ways about a potentially old topic. Many students with exposure to chemistry come in with chemistry vocabulary and some ideas – they are often able to arrive at the "correct answer" to a question. But experience has taught us that most of these students do not understand the concepts behind the words. They may use the word "molecule" or "bond" but may not have an accurate conceptual understanding to accompany the word. With this curriculum you'll even the playing field by bringing everyone along, from your poorest students to your most gifted ones, and build a common foundation of understanding.

Finally, your role in the classroom changes as you work with the curriculum. Student-centered curriculum is precisely that – centered on the learner. The activities in *Living By Chemistry* are based in guided inquiry. You are their guide. Students complete an activity every day, often working in pairs or teams of four. As your students inquire and explore, you'll develop a more dynamic, in-the-present instruction style. Sometimes you'll feel that you have a little less control in the classroom as ideas fly around the room. Many times the exploratory process will generate questions you can't answer right away. Both of these are likely possibilities with this curriculum. But feel secure in the knowledge that these are some of the signs of a fertile, successful learning environment. It is up to you to foster this active curiosity and to make the classroom a safe place not only for new ideas and interesting hypotheses but also for wild ideas and shaky hypotheses, as well as routine inaccuracies, misconceptions, and simplistic questions. Students using the *LBC* curriculum are grateful for the group input, reporting that they benefit from a wider variety of strategies and approaches to a problem, rather than a single approach presented by an instructor. Eventually, your classroom may seem to run itself. As students work cooperatively on the challenges you set for them, you will be free address the individual needs of different learners.

Overview of Unit Structure and Lesson Design

Living By Chemistry is a full-year high school chemistry curriculum that meets state and national standards. The entire curriculum consists of six units organized around content. A single contextual theme runs throughout each unit, enhancing students' understanding of the chemistry content. The context provides a real-world foundation for the chemistry concepts and holds the students' interest.

Each unit consists of 25–30 lessons of 50-minute duration each. These daily lessons are clustered into 4 or 5 investigations. Each investigation addresses a piece of the content that students need for a full understanding of the context-based question asked at the beginning of the unit.

The lessons follow a standard format designed to support a guided inquiry approach to teaching and learning. The main parts are Exploring the Topic, Activity, Making Sense Discussion, and Check-in. Here are the goals of these instructional components.

Exploring the Topic: The main goal of this section is to activate students' current thoughts, beliefs, and understanding on a specific topic. Upon starting class, you immediately engage students in an exercise, one that focuses them on the main goal of the lesson and generates interest. We call this exercise the ChemCatalyst. Once the students have answered the question individually, a class discussion ensues. This discussion is an opportunity for you to find out what your students think. We recommend that you listen to student ideas and ask for explanations, without judgment.

Activity: Each lesson has an activity to allow students to work with the day's ideas and gather further information about the topic. The activities are quite varied, and include experiments, card sorts, worksheets with problems, model building, etc. Generally, you'll have the students work in small groups. You circulate from group to group, offering evidence, and guiding students to refine their ideas. We recommend that you avoid giving your students answers. Instead give them a chance to think and build their own understanding.

Making Sense Discussion: The main goal of this part of the lesson is to assist students in formalizing their understanding. This is a chance to engage the class as a whole in processing the activity, with the goal of illuminating some new chemistry concepts, ideas, tools, or definitions. We recommend that you get the class to provide evidence for the key ideas, using information gathered in the activity.

Check-in: A question is posed to provide both you and your students with a quick assessment of their grasp of the day's concepts.

The lesson structure supports the investigative process: students are engaged with the ChemCatalyst, they explore their ideas in the Activity, and they explain and elaborate on their ideas in the Making Sense Discussion. Evaluation and monitoring of understanding is embedded throughout.

One common question is: How much time does this take? First of all, the preparation for each class is different. Instead of spending time creating a lesson, you will be spending time setting up activities. During the class, instead of lecturing, you will be mainly interacting with students and guiding their explorations. Finally, hands-on and minds-on learning may seem slow at first. However, because students retain and understand the ideas more fully, the amount you can cover increases as the year progresses. We believe it is possible to surpass state and national standards.

Teacher's Materials and Kit

The *Living By Chemistry* curriculum comes with a student guide, a detailed teacher's guide, and a kit with supplies that are not typically found in a chemistry classroom. The teacher's guide has step-by-step instructions for each lesson. Here are some highlights of what is contained in these materials:

- ChemCatalyst and Check-in questions
- Student worksheets for each lesson
- Sample questions to ask students in discussions along with typical student responses
- Pages to photocopy onto transparencies for use in class discussions
- Detailed descriptions of the set-up for each lesson
- Supplies that cannot be purchased in a store
- A list of supplies that are not included

Conclusion

Our preliminary field-test results suggest that student performance improves with the *Living By Chemistry* curriculum. One of the most gratifying comments that we hear frequently from teachers is that they find many more students participating, including those who were not participating previously. We hope your experience with the curriculum meets these expectations.

The *Living By Chemistry* Development Team

***Fire* Unit –** Main Topics Covered

Covered in Depth

Temperature and heat flow

Exothermic and endothermic processes

Energy associated with phase changes

Heat flow problems. specific heat capacity, latent heat

Enthalpy of reaction, Hess's law

Catalyst

Activation energy

Prerequisites for the *Fire* Unit

Periodic table, atomic number, atomic mass

Chemical reactions

Fire Unit

Kit Inventory List

2 **alcohol burners**
matches (1 large box, 16 small boxes, and 1 box long matches)[1]
16 long lab **candles**[1]
1 short lab **candle**[1]
3.5 feet of **plastic tubing** (~1/4-inch diameter)
100 surgical **gloves**[1]
magnets

pads of **steel wool** (very fine)[1]
liquid soap[1]
48 **plastic spoons**
100 large **paper clips**
300 **balloons**[1]
20–30 square feet of **aluminum foil**[1]
1 small lump of **clay**
300 **cotton balls**[1]

2 large bags **Cheetos**®[1]

[1] Consumable; will need to be replenished. This kit includes enough for approximately 2-3 years, or up to 10 classes of 32 students.

For up-to-date information about kit contents, please visit www.keypress.com/chemistry.

To order new kits, contact:

Key Curriculum Press
1150 65th Street
Emeryville, CA 94608
(800) 995-6284   www.keypress.com

To report errors or problems, please call us or send an e-mail to editorial@keypress.com

Fire Unit – Other Materials Needed

An attempt has been made to provide the specialized items needed for each lab. However, common lab ware, chemicals, and other easily obtainable materials have not been included in this kit. They are listed in the "Other materials needed" column.

Quantities specified assume a class size of 32 students. You will need to change the quantities according to your class size.

SAFETY NOTE: In this unit, we will be burning numerous substances to find out more about fire. The experiments that will be carried out have been selected because they allow for the safe observation of fire. However, caution is always essential when dealing with not wear loose clothing; put out small fires by smothering the flames with a fire blanket, water, or sand; etc.)
Have a fire extinguisher available at all times. Remember that a carbon dioxide fire extinguisher and water cannot be used for fires caused by metals. Make sure students know where to get help quickly should the need arise.
A clay pot filled with sand is useful for extinguishing metal fires. Burning items can be plunged into the sand to extinguish them, or sand can be poured onto a fire.
Remind students of the importance of lab safety at the outset of this unit. You may wish to establish that any deviation from procedures will result in loss of lab credit or lab privileges.

Lab Ware (Per class of 32 students)
32 safety goggles (1 per student)
1 pair tongs
16 ring stands with clamps
1 propane lighter or Bunsen burner
8 hot plates
8 scale balances
1 fireproof surface
1 50-mL beaker
24 100-mL beakers
3 500-mL beakers
1 1000-mL beaker
1 250-mL Erlenmeyer flask
2 test tubes (optional)
8 watch glasses
1 long glass rod (~4 feet)
1 glass stirring rod (~1 foot)
16 thermometers
1 funnel

Chemicals (for ten classes of 32 students)
60 g aluminum powder, Al
40 g copper powder, Cu
250 g iron powder, Fe
10 g magnesium pieces, Mg
20 g magnesium powder, Mg
240 g ammonium chloride, NH_4Cl
650 g barium nitrate, $Ba(NO_3)_2$
240 g calcium chloride, $CaCl_2$
1000 mL 1 M hydrochloric acid, HCl
10 mL concentrated sulfuric acid (18M)
250 g potassium chlorate, $KClO_3$
60 g potassium nitrate, KNO_3
325 g strontium nitrate, $Sr(NO_3)_2$
500 mL rubbing alcohol
800 g sodium chloride, NaCl (21 tsp.)

Other Materials (for 10 classes of 32 students)	
Baking flour	1 dollar bill (optional)
Water	1 dowel or broom handle
200 g sugar	1 clay flower pot with sand
10 intact eggshells with the contents blown out	1 piece of chalk
500 mL lamp oil	1 wide, shallow plastic dish
1 tsp salt	1 tray (for minimal clean-up)
500 mL vinegar	1 250-mL plastic cup
160 g cornstarch	String (~1 foot)
1000 paper clips	Tape
16 empty tuna fish cans (optional; other containers may be substituted)	Masking tape
16 empty soda cans with tabs	Scissors
32 pieces of wire (8–10") cut from hangers	Elmer's glue or glue sticks
1 piece of iron wire (6"; cut from hangers)	1 sheet poster paper or butcher paper for Fire concept map
1 9-volt battery	2 oven mitts (can be found in Weather kit)
2 wires with alligator clips	

Lesson-by-Lesson Lab Guide

Materials listed here are for a class of 32 students.

Lesson I-1: Fired Up

Preparation: Prepare some soapy water in the shallow plastic dish. Use enough soap so that blowing into it with a straw produces soap bubbles.
If you do not have Bunsen burners, you may use a lighter.
Tape a long candle to the end of a dowel or broom handle.

Materials Provided in Kit	Other Materials Needed
1 long kitchen match	Student worksheet
1 small box matches	32 safety goggles (1 per student)
1 short lab candle	1 propane lighter or Bunsen burner
1 long lab candle (attach to dowel or broom handle)	1 methane gas outlet with tube attached
1 alcohol burner (fill with rubbing alcohol)	1 ring stand
1 cotton ball	1 watch glass
1 pair gloves	1 beaker with 50 mL rubbing alcohol
1 balloon (inflate)	2 100-mL beakers
Liquid soap	1 pair tongs
	1 fireproof surface
	1 glass stirring rod (~1 foot)
	4.5 g potassium chlorate, $KClO_3$
	1 mL concentrated sulfuric acid (18 M)
	20 g sugar
	1 piece of iron wire (~6" long); may be cut from hanger
	1 plastic cup or bottle (~250 mL)
	1 tray (to minimize clean-up)
	1 wide, shallow plastic dish
	water
	tape

Lesson I-2: Hot and Cold

Preparation: Set up $CaCl_2$, NaCl, and NH_4Cl in beakers at each table.

Materials Provided in Kit	Other Materials Needed
24 plastic spoons	Student worksheet
	32 safety goggles (1 pair per student)

(cont.)

	8 100-mL beakers
	24 beakers for salts
	24 g ammonium chloride, NH_4Cl
	24 g calcium chloride, $CaCl_2$
	24 g sodium chloride, NaCl
	8 thermometers
	water

Lesson I-4: Now We're Cookin'

Preparation: Students will skewer a Cheeto puff on the end of a straightened paperclip and burn it in this calorimetry experiment. They will need a holder for the burning Cheeto. Taping the other end of the paperclip to an empty tuna can works well; other stands can be improvised depending on what you have available.
You may wish to devise one calorimetry setup at the front of the room as an example for students to follow. You may also wish to open some windows for increased ventilation.

Materials Provided in Kit	Other Materials Needed
1 bag Cheeto® puffs (at least 16 pieces)	32 safety goggles (1 pair per student)
2–3 boxes of matches	Student worksheet
	16 ring stands with clamps
	16 thermometers
	16 empty tuna fish cans (or other containers)
	16 empty soda cans with tabs
	1 roll aluminum foil
	100 paper clips
	2 L water
	tape

Lesson II-1: No Smoking Zone

ALERT: In order to complete this activity a cigarette will be lit and "smoked" by an apparatus. Thus, you should make sure that students are not asthmatic or allergic to cigarette smoke prior to the demonstration. Open windows, if possible.

Preparation: Construct your "smoking machine" before class. Use a plastic soda bottle with a cap. Carefully cut a small hole in the bottle cap and insert the tubing through the hole. Use clay around the base of the tubing to completely seal the hole in the cap. Insert an unfiltered cigarette into the other end of the tubing. Place a few cotton balls inside the bottle. Keep at least one fresh cotton ball for comparison. Following the directions in the Teacher Guide, practice using the machine before using it in class.

Materials Provided in Kit	Other Materials Needed
1 piece of 6-inch plastic tubing (Cut one 6-inch piece from plastic tubing; save 3 feet for Lesson II-6)	32 safety goggles (1 pair per student)

(cont.)

Small lump of clay to seal hole in cap	1 500-mL beaker with 50 mL water, labeled "water"
5–6 cotton balls	1 500-mL beaker with 50 mL isopropanol (rubbing alcohol), labeled "isopropanol"
Matches	1 500-mL beaker with 25 mL water mixed with 25 mL isopropanol, labeled "50/50 water/isopropanol"
1 balloon (blow up and label "CO_2")	1 pair tongs
1 long candle (tape to dowel or broom handle)	1 package unfiltered cigarettes, or cigarettes with the filters cut off (1-2 cigarettes per class)*
	1 clay flower pot with sand (for putting out paper fire)
	3 paper strips, ~3" x 11" each
	dollar bill (optional, for effect; strip of paper may be used instead)
	1 plastic 2-L bottle with cap
	tape

*Optional: Paper or tissue paper rolled to the size of a cigarette may be substituted.

Lesson II-2: You're Fired!

Preparation: Fill a clean empty alcohol burner with lamp oil.

Materials Provided in Kit	Other Materials Needed
1 alcohol burner	32 safety goggles (1 per student)
1 small piece of steel wool	1 watch glass
1 candle (Bunsen burner may be used instead)	1 thermometer
matches	50 mL lamp oil
12-inch piece aluminum foil	50 mL vinegar (optional, to clean steel wool)
	1 teaspoon of salt
	1 piece of chalk
	2 oven mitts (can be found in Weather kit)

Lesson II-4: Fuelish Choices

Materials provided in kit	Other materials needed
	Fire Concept Map from Lesson I-6

Lesson II-5: Sparklers

Preparation: Cut the wire hangers using wire cutters (provided in the Alchemy kit). Set up the various powders and compounds at each table or at stations around the room. DANGER: DO NOT USE POTASSIUM PERCHLORATE IN THIS EXPERIMENT.

SAFETY NOTE: Although sparklers are legal in most states, they are banned in some states and counties. Check with your local fire marshal to determine whether you can do this activity with your class.

Materials Provided in Kit	Other Materials Needed
8 surgical gloves	32 safety goggles (1 per student)
	2 large beakers
	8 hot plates
	8 balances
	8 watch glasses
	6 g aluminum powder, Al
	65 g barium nitrate, $Ba(NO_3)_2$
	4 g copper powder, Cu
	25 g iron powder, Fe
	2 g magnesium powder, Mg
	16 g potassium chlorate, $KClO_3$
	33 g strontium nitrate, $Sr(NO_3)_2$
	16 g cornstarch
	40 mL water
	32 pieces of wire (8–10") cut from hangers

Preparation for next day: If the sparklers are not too thick or too runny, they will air-dry overnight if stuck upright in a beaker. If they need some assistance, a fan or a blow dryer on a low setting can be used to dry them.
Hollow out an eggshell for each class (see Preparation for II-6).

Lesson II-6: Kablooie!

Preparation: Retrieve the oven-dried sparklers that students made in Lesson II-5. Inflate a balloon.
You will also need a hollow eggshell for each class, to demonstrate the spectacular combustion of methane. Use a pin to make a small hole (less than 1 cm in diameter) in the top and bottom of an egg and break the yolk, and blow out the contents into a bowl. Rinse out the shell and allow it to dry.
Cut out and assemble a fire tetrahedron (see handout).
You may also wish to "load" the surgical tubing with flour before class.

Materials Provided in Kit	Other Materials Needed
Surgical tubing or long pipette	32 safety goggles (1 per student)
Candle (Bunsen burner may be used instead)	Natural gas used for Bunsen burners (to fill eggshell)

(cont.)

Matches	1 ring stand
Balloon (fill with air)	1 funnel
	Intact eggshell with contents blown out
	Baking flour
	String
	Push pin
	Fire Map on butcher paper from Lesson I-6
	Scissors
	Elmer's glue or glue sticks
	Candle (attach to wooden dowel or broom handle)

Lesson III-1: No Going Back

Preparation: Fill a balloon with hydrogen by reacting magnesium in hydrochloric acid. Place about 100 mL of 1M HCl in a 250 mL Erlenmeyer flask. Put magnesium pieces (~1.0 g) inside a balloon. Put the balloon over the mouth of the flask without allowing the magnesium to fall into the HCl. Once the balloon is securely sealed around the flask, shake the deflated balloon to allow the magnesium to drop into the flask. The reaction between the magnesium and HCl generates H_2 gas, which inflates the balloon to about 1 liter. Once the reaction is complete, tie off the balloon. Since the balloon is less dense than air, be sure to tie a string onto the balloon so that you do not lose it. Hydrogen balloons can be made the morning before their use. They don't "save" well overnight.

Set up water electrolysis. Put about 800 mL of water in a 1000 mL beaker. Add about 15 teaspoons salt. Stir until all the salt dissolves. Fold two 8 cm x 8 cm pieces of aluminum foil so that you have two flat strips about 8 cm x 1 cm. Hang the two strips from the side of the beaker. Do not allow the two strips to touch one another.

Materials Provided in Kit	**Other Materials Needed**
1 balloon (to fill with H_2 gas)	1 250-mL Erlenmeyer flask
Matches	1 1000-mL beaker
2 pieces of aluminum foil (~8 cm x 8 cm)	2 test tubes (to collect gases)
	1 ring stand with ring
	100 mL 1 M hydrochloric acid
	1 g magnesium pieces
	800 mL salt water w/ 60 g salt (15 teaspoons)
	1 9-volt battery
	2 wires with alligator clips
	String (~1 foot)
	Candle (attach to wooden dowel or broom handle)

Preparation for next day: Prepare a sign for each class, with "Fire" written in invisible ink (see Preparation for III-2).

Lesson III-2: Fire Starter

Preparation: For each class, prepare a sign that says "Fire" in invisible ink for the demonstration. In a small beaker, add potassium nitrate (about 6 g) to 20 mL of water until you have created a saturated solution. Use a glass stirring rod or a cotton swab to write the word "Fire" on the paper. Make sure that you use cursive or continuous writing so that the letters are all connected to each other. Use plenty of solution and make the lines thick. Put a small mark on the paper where the word begins, for later reference. Let the paper dry at room temperature.

Materials Provided in Kit	Other Materials Needed
2 magnets	32 safety goggles (1 per student)
Matches	1 50-mL beaker
	1 stirring rod
	~6 g potassium nitrate, KNO_3
	20 mL water
	1 piece of uncoated paper (~8.5" x 11")
	Masking tape

Lesson III-4: Ashes to Ashes

Materials Provided in Kit	Other Materials Needed
	Student worksheet
	Fire concept map

Living By Chemistry

Unit 5: Fire

Unit Feedback Form

Your feedback is valuable to us, even if you do not answer every question. Once you have filled out this form, all you have to do is fold it and drop it in the mail. We'll pay the postage. Thank you!

Was it easy for you and your students to understand the objectives of this unit? ____________

1. Do you think that the unit met all of its objectives? ____________

____

____

2. Rate the difficulty of this unit. ❑ Too difficult ❑ Too easy ❑ About right

   Comments: ____________

   ____

3. Was too much or too little time spent on any topic? Please comment: ____________

   Too much: ____________

   Too little: ____________

4. What topics were *not* included in this unit, but should have been in order to satisfy your state or district standards? ____________

   ____

5. What kinds of material did you add to this unit? ____________

   ____

6. Compared to your previous curriculum, did students learn concepts more thoroughly or less thoroughly with this unit? ❑ More thoroughly ❑ Less thoroughly ❑ About the same

   Please comment: ____________

   What criteria did you use to answer this question? ____________

   ____

7. How would you describe your overall experience with the unit?

   ❑ very positive ❑ positive ❑ fair ❑ negative ❑ very negative

   Comments: ____________

   ____

8. What changes would you make to this unit? ____________

   ____

9. What activities or lessons were most successful? Why? ____________

   ____

Submitted by: ____________ Date: ____________

May we contact you to further discuss your experiences? Yes ❑ No ❑

If yes, please include the best way to reach you:

Phone ____________ E-mail____________

Please detach page, fold on lines and tape edge.

NO POSTAGE NECESSARY IF MAILED IN THE UNITED STATES

BUSINESS REPLY MAIL
FIRST CLASS PERMIT NO. 338 OAKLAND, CA

POSTAGE WILL BE PAID BY ADDRESSEE

KEY CURRICULUM PRESS
1150 65TH STREET
EMERYVILLE CA 94608-9740

Attention Editorial: *Living By Chemistry*

Living By Chemistry
Unit 5: Fire

Correction/Comment Form

Please help us correct and improve *Living By Chemistry.* If you find mistakes in the Teacher Guide or Student Guide, use this form to let us know. If you have further comments or suggestions about the materials, we'd like to hear those as well.

Once you've filled out this form, all you have to do is fold it and drop it in the mail. We'll pay the postage. Thank you!

Your Name ______________________________

School ______________________________

School Address ______________________________

City/State/Zip ______________________________

Phone ______________________________

Teacher Guide:

Page ____________ Comment ______________________________

Page ____________ Comment ______________________________

Page ____________ Comment ______________________________

Page ____________ Comment ______________________________

Page ____________ Comment ______________________________

Page ____________ Comment ______________________________

Student Guide:

Page ____________ Comment ______________________________

Page ____________ Comment ______________________________

Page ____________ Comment ______________________________

Page ____________ Comment ______________________________

Page ____________ Comment ______________________________

Page ____________ Comment ______________________________

Do you have any general comments about *Living By Chemistry,* or any suggestions for improving the student or teacher material? (Please use the Unit Feedback Form if you wish to give more extensive feedback.)

____

____

____

Please detach page, fold on lines and tape edge.

NO POSTAGE
NECESSARY
IF MAILED
IN THE
UNITED STATES

BUSINESS REPLY MAIL
FIRST CLASS PERMIT NO. 338 OAKLAND, CA

POSTAGE WILL BE PAID BY ADDRESSEE

KEY CURRICULUM PRESS
1150 65TH STREET
EMERYVILLE CA 94608-9740

Attention Editorial: *Living By Chemistry*

Unit 5: Fire

Investigation I: Evidence of Change

Contents of Investigation I *Page*

Investigation I Summary:

Evidence of Change

Lesson 1 – Fired Up This lesson introduces students to the Fire Unit. Fire is a complex phenomenon. Before students can understand fire they must spend some time observing its behavior, describing it, and developing their communication skills on the topic. In this class, students observe a series of demonstrations that involve fire. They observe the types of changes that take place. They are specifically asked to notice if the procedures involve heat and light, and if new products form.

Lesson 2 – Hot and Cold In this activity students take a closer look at what it means to be hot or cold. They begin by discussing what we mean when we say a fire warms us. Then students measure the temperature changes that occur upon dissolving three different salts in water. The results are translated onto graphs for easier interpretation and comparison. Students are introduced to the words exothermic and endothermic as they relate the temperature changes they observed to heat transfer either from the solution to the environment or from the environment into the solution.

Lesson 3 – Point of View This activity assists students in looking at the transfer of heat from different points of view. It is easy to become confused about heat transfer unless one specifies the point of view that is being referred to. Students gain practice articulating the relationship between the directionality of heat transfer, what they would observe or experience, and what the system "experiences." The term "system" is introduced to assist students in conceptualizing heat transfer.

Lesson 4 – Now We're Cookin' Students continue their exploration of heat transfer by completing a calorimetry experiment involving the heating of water by burning Cheetos®. Students will investigate how heat transfer relates to the mass of the Cheeto® as well as to the mass of the water being heated. This activity is processed in greater detail in the following lesson.

Lesson 5 – Fat Calories In this lesson, students analyze further the data they obtained in yesterday's experiment. The calorie is introduced as a measure of heat. Students use the definition of a calorie to analyze the heat transfer in the calorimetry experiment. The calories absorbed by the water depend on the specific heat capacity of water, the mass of water heated, and the magnitude of the temperature change. The burning Cheeto® released the calories absorbed by the water. The lesson ends with a discussion of food Calories and how they are determined.

Lesson 6 – Burning Questions In this lesson, students gain practice in solving problems involving heat transfer. The problems include heating substances other than water and the heat required for phase changes. Specific heat capacities for various substances are compared, and the heat associated with phase changes (latent heat) is introduced. As various substances, amounts, and temperature changes are examined, the focus becomes understanding the difference between heat and temperature in terms of the motions of atoms. The lesson ends with a summary of the *Fire* unit thus far.

BEFORE CLASS...

LESSON 1 – Fired Up

Key Ideas:
For millennia fire has been a vital energy source for humankind. Fire is a chemical change that transfers energy as heat and light. New products, such as ash, smoke, and gases, form as the fire burns. There is an association between fire, chemical change and heat exchange.

What Takes Place:
Students observe a series of demonstrations aimed at giving them an opportunity to discuss and describe fires caused by various reactions. Based on their observations, students list the demonstrations that produce a fire, and discuss the changes that take place. They look for common characteristics of a fire. Students consider the association of fire with heat and light, and the formation of new products.

Materials: (For each class)

- Student worksheet
- 1 long kitchen match
- 1 small box matches
- 1 candle (preferably a short, wide candle that does not tip over easily)
- 1 watch glass
- 1 piece of iron wire (~6" long; may be cut from coat hanger)
- 1 alcohol burner
- 50 mL of isopropanol (rubbing alcohol)
- 1 beaker for isopropanol
- 1 cotton ball
- 1 pair tongs
- 4.5 g $KClO_3$, potassium chlorate
- 20.0 g of sugar
- 1 plastic cup (~250 mL)
- 1 fireproof surface
- 1 mL concentrated sulfuric acid (18 M)
- 2 100-mL beakers
- 1 glass stirring rod (~1 ft)
- 1 tray (to minimize clean-up)
- 1 pair gloves
- 1 propane lighter or Bunsen burner attached to a gas outlet
- 1 wide, shallow plastic dish
- soapy water

- 1 candle taped to a wooden dowel or broom handle
- 1 balloon
- 1 ringstand
- tape
- 1 straw

Investigation I – Evidence of Change

LESSON 1 – Fired Up

This lesson introduces students to the *Fire* unit. Fire is a complex phenomenon. Before students can understand fire they must spend some time observing its behavior, describing it, and developing their communication skills on the topic. In this class, students observe a series of demonstrations that involve fire. They observe the types of changes that take place. They are specifically asked to notice if the procedures involve heat and light, and if new products form.

Exploring the Topic (5–10 min)

1. Introduce the ChemCatalyst exercise.

Write the following exercise on the board for students to complete individually.

Several people are left on a remote, deserted island with only the clothes on their backs. They must survive on their own. One of the first tasks they all agree on is to try and build a fire.

- Why is fire so vital to their survival?
- Describe a fire.
- Is fire still vital to our survival? Explain.

2. Discuss the ChemCatalyst exercise.

Use the discussion to get a sense of students' initial ideas.

Discussion goals:
Use the students' written responses to stimulate an open-ended discussion of fire in order to engage them in the context and sample their understanding.

Sample questions:
Why is fire so useful to human beings?
What does fire provide us with?
What things wouldn't we have without fire?
What is fire? What is your evidence?
Where does fire come from?
How would you describe fire to someone who had never experienced it?
What is happening to matter in a fire?

At this stage we just want to find out what students think. You may let the discussion range as far as you want, as long as it remains centered around fire. Many of us use the heat generated from burning natural gas to heat our water, heat our homes, and cook our food. Some students may realize that coal-burning power plants provide much of the nation's electricity and that the internal combustion engine found in the automobile utilizes fire. Some may say that we would not have pollution if we didn't have fire.

3. Explain safety procedures.

Points to cover:
Safety note: In this unit, we will be burning numerous substances to find out more about fire. The experiments that will be carried out have been selected because they allow for the observation of fire safely. However, caution is always essential when dealing with fire. Make sure that hair is tied back. Do not wear loose clothing. Put out small fires by smothering the flames with a fire blanket, water, or sand. Have a fire extinguisher available at all times. Remember that a carbon dioxide fire extinguisher and water cannot be used for fires caused by metals. Know where to get help quickly should the need arise.

4. Explain the purpose of today's activity.

If you wish you can write the main question on the board. If you wish, enlist a few students to help with today's demonstrations.

Points to cover:
Tell students that today they will complete a series of laboratory procedures so that they can begin to think about fire. They will be making observations to assist them in giving a preliminary answer to the question, "What are the characteristics of fire?"

Activity – Fired Up (15 min)

5. Introduce the activity. (Worksheet)

Pass out the worksheet and explain the activity. Give students a chance to fill out the table in the worksheet as you do the demonstrations.

Most of these demonstrations are easy to set up. You can choose to do all or only some of them.

Safety note: Wear safety glasses while performing these demonstrations. Keep hair and loose clothing away from flames. Make sure students are at least 10 feet away from the demonstration table. Be sure to have a fire extinguisher available.

Demonstrations:

DEMO 1 – Match

Materials:
1 long kitchen match

Strike a long kitchen match. Hold the match so students can observe. Discuss what would extinguish the flame and let students speculate as to why.

DEMO 2 – Candle

Materials:
1 candle (preferably a short, wide candle that does not tip over easily)
1 match
1 watch glass
1 piece of iron wire (~6" long)

Light a candle. Place a piece of glass over the flame in order to collect some of the carbon that is produced. Move the wire slowly up and down in the flame to determine were the flame is the hottest as judged by how bright the wire glows. (The burning candle produces a yellow flame.)

DEMO 3 – Alcohol burner

Materials:
1 alcohol burner
50 mL of isopropanol (rubbing alcohol)
1 match
1 piece of iron wire (~6" long)

Pour 50 mL of isopropanol into the alcohol burner. Light the burner. Move the wire slowly up and down in the flame to determine where the flame is the hottest. (The burning isopropanol produces a blue flame.)

DEMO 4 – Alcohol cotton ball

Materials:
1 cotton ball
1 beaker with ~50 mL isopropanol (rubbing alcohol)
1 pair tongs
1 lit candle

Hold a cotton ball with tongs. Dip the cotton ball in isopropanol. Allow some isopropanol to evaporate so that there is no liquid dripping from the cotton ball. Take the cotton ball to a candle that is at some distance from the beaker with the isopropanol. Ignite the cotton ball with the candle.

DEMO 5 – Sugar sparks

Materials:
4.5 g $KClO_3$, potassium chlorate
9.0 g of sugar
1 plastic cup (~250 mL)
1 fireproof surface
1 glass stirring rod taped to a stick (~4 ft)
1 drop concentrated sulfuric acid

Carefully mix 4.5 g potassium chlorate and 9.0 g sugar in a plastic container. Pour the mixture onto a fireproof surface such as a wire mesh with gauze or a fireproof tile. Make a small depression in the middle of the pile with a spatula. Dip a long-handled glass rod (~4 ft) into concentrated sulfuric acid so that there is a drop of acid on the tip of the rod. Standing at a distance, touch the tip of the glass rod to the pile of potassium chlorate and sugar. Stand back. (The reaction starts slowly, evolving smoke and then flames. The flames are lavender due to the presence of potassium.)

DEMO 6 – Caramelized sugar

Materials:
10 g of sugar
10 mL concentrated sulfuric acid
2 100-mL beaker
1 glass stirring rod (~1 ft)
1 tray (to minimize clean-up)
1 pair gloves

Wear gloves. Put about 10 g of sugar into a 100 mL beaker. Place the beaker on a tray to aid in clean-up. Add about 10 mL of concentrated sulfuric acid. Stir briefly with a glass rod (you can leave the glass rod in the beaker). Stand back and watch the reaction. (A black column of carbon will grow. Hot steam is also produced. Be careful to protect yourself from burns.)

DEMO 7 – Bunsen burner

Materials:
1 Bunsen burner attached to a gas outlet (if gas outlets are not available, you may use a propane lighter)
1 piece of iron wire
1 match

Light the Bunsen burner. Move the wire slowly up and down in the flame to determine where the flame is the hottest. (The burning methane produces a blue flame.)

DEMO 8 – Bursting bubbles

Materials:
1 methane gas outlet with a tube attached (if gas outlets are not available, you may use a propane lighter)
1 wide, shallow plastic dish
soapy water
1 candle taped to a wooden dowel
1 straw

Place a few inches of soapy water in a large plastic bowl. Bubble natural gas (from the gas outlets used for the Bunsen burner) through the water just long enough to create a few bubbles on top of the soapy water. Turn the gas off. Attach a tapered candle to a wooden dowel so that you can stand at a distance to ignite the bubbles. (You will see tiny flames where the bubble burst.)

As a control, blow bubbles in the soapy water through a straw. Bring a candle close to show that the bubbles pop, but there is no explosion.

DEMO 9 – Air balloon

Materials:
1 balloon
1 ringstand
tape
1 candle taped to a wooden dowel

Blow up a balloon. Attach the balloon with tape to the top of a ringstand. Attach a tapered candle to a wooden dowel so that you can stand at a distance. Hold the flame to the balloon to make it pop.

Worksheet

Instructions: You will observe several demonstrations. Place a check in the table if you observe heat, light, and/or fire.

		Heat	Light	Fire	Products
1	match	√	√	√	yellow flame, smoke
2	candle	√	√	√	yellow flames, smoke
3	alcohol burner	√	√	√	blue flame
4	alcohol cotton balls	√	√	√	yellow flame
5	sugar sparks	√	√	√	white sparks
6	carmelized sugar	√	√		black substance, steam
7	Bunsen burner	√	√	√	blue flame
8	bursting bubbles	√	√	√	flame
9	air balloon				popped balloon

Answer the following questions:

1. Which reactions produced a fire? Why did you classify them as fire producing?
2. Which reactions did not produce a fire? Why did you classify them as non-fire producing?
3. A student argues that Reaction 6 produced a fire because it resulted in a pile of burnt, black material and the smell of burnt sugar. Do you agree? Why or why not?
4. What evidence do you have that new products have formed after a fire has occurred?
5. What evidence do you have that heat and the formation of new products are associated with one another?

Making sense:
List three characteristics of fire.

If you finish early…
Procedure 9 produced an explosion, but there was no fire. Explain how a fire and an explosion are different.

Making Sense Discussion (10 min)

Major goals: One of the main goals of this discussion is to provide students with the opportunity to communicate about the changes they observed, and to begin to develop a common language of heat, fire, and energy. Students should come away from this lesson with the idea that fire is the result of a chemical change and that fire is energy released in the form of heat and light. In addition, this lesson is intended to spark an interest in the context of this unit and lay out its general goals.

6. Discuss the changes that were observed.

Write the word "Observations" on the board and keep track of the various changes the students observed.

Discussion goals:
Assist the students in verbalizing the changes they observed.

Sample questions:
Describe some of the changes that you observed.
Which changes could you detect with your sense of touch, vision, hearing, and smell?
What do you suppose smoke is?

Are new products formed after a fire? Explain your thinking.
Can you always see the products of a fire? Explain.
Is fire the result of a chemical reaction? How can you tell?

Possible Observations:

Bright light / flame	Smell
Heat / warmth	Sound
Smoke	Ashes / soot
Charred substance	Chemical change

Points to cover:
We depend a great deal on our senses to tell us what is happening in the chemistry laboratory. Our eyes tell us when we see flames, our skin tells us when we feel an increase in temperature, our nose tells us when we smell smoke or burning, and so on. But our senses can only provide us with a partial picture of what is really going on when fire occurs. We will have to go deeper than our senses if we wish to truly understand fire and the relationship between energy and change.

7. Introduce the *Fire* unit.

Discussion goals:
Assist students in creating a beginning definition for fire based on what they've learned and observed so far.

Sample questions:
How would you define fire based on your laboratory experiences so far?
Is a fire the result of a chemical reaction? What evidence do you have to support your answer?
What evidence do you have to suggest that heat and chemical change are associated with one another?

Points to cover:
We are just beginning our exploration of fire and we have a lot of chemistry to investigate. It is apparent that fire involves a release of energy. We can feel and see this energy in the heat and light we sense from a fire.

It is apparent that fire is the result of a chemical reaction – we can tell this because new substances with new properties are produced by fire. (Sometimes the reactants seem to disappear because colorless, odorless gases are formed.) Students don't yet know which chemical reactions these are or how we would be able to recognize a possible "fire reaction" before it happened. Students don't know what makes these reactions different from other chemical reactions, or why so much energy is released with a fire. We will be exploring all of these unanswered questions, and more, as we move through the *Fire* unit.

Fire: A fire is the result of a chemical change or chemical reaction. A fire releases energy in the form of light and heat. New products are formed. Smoke, ashes, or explosions can sometimes accompany fires.

8. Relate the topic of fire to the concept of energy.

Give a preliminary definition of the word energy.

Discussion goals:
Assist students in creating a beginning definition for energy based on their use of the word in daily language.

Sample questions:
What do you think energy is?
What do you mean when you say you have energy?
Do you think energy is a thing you possess or a property? Explain?

Points to cover:
The concept of energy is the main theme in the *Fire* unit. Despite the fact that we use the word energy in our daily language, it is difficult to define. We say we have energy when we feel like we are able to "get up and go," to move around, to run fast, to work hard. In this way, energy is a property that we have that enables motion, not a thing that we possess. We also say that fire releases energy. As we move through the unit, the connection between fire, energy, and motion will become clearer.

Check-in (5 min)

9. No Check-in for this class.

10. Wrap-up

Assist the students in summarizing what was learned in the class.

- A fire is the result of a chemical reaction.
- A fire releases energy in the form of light and heat.
- New products are formed as the result of a fire.
- Chemical change and heat are associated with one another.

Homework

11. Assign homework.

Use the homework provided with the curriculum or assign your own.

Homework – Investigation I – Lesson 1

1. Write two or three paragraphs describing how you think fire was discovered and how it's discovery might have changed life for human beings back in prehistoric times.
2. What kinds of things does fire make possible in your life?
3. What would you do if you were stranded on a desert island and you wanted to try to make fire?
4. Write out four questions you have about fire.

Fired Up

Student Worksheet

Name: ______________________

Date: ______________________

Purpose: This lesson provides first hand experience with fire.

Instructions: You will observe several demonstrations. Place a check in the table if you observe heat, light, and/or fire.

		Heat	Light	Fire	Products
1	match				
2	candle				
3	alcohol burner				
4	alcohol cotton balls				
5	sugar sparks				
6	caramelized sugar				
7	Bunsen burner				
8	bursting bubbles				
9	air balloon				

Answer the following questions:

1. Which reactions produced a fire? Why did you classify them as fire producing?

2. Which reactions did not produce a fire? Why did you classify them as non–fire producing?

3. A student argues that Reaction 6 produced a fire because it resulted in a pile of burnt, black material and the smell of burnt sugar. Do you agree? Why or why not?

4. What evidence do you have that new products have formed after a fire has occurred?

5. What evidence do you have that heat and the formation of new products are associated with one another?

Making sense:

List three characteristics of fire.

If you finish early…

Procedure 9 produced an explosion, but there was no fire. Explain how a fire and an explosion are different.

BEFORE CLASS…

LESSON 2 – Hot and Cold

Key Ideas:
Heat transfer is the result of a temperature difference. When a hotter object comes in contact with a colder object, heat is transferred from the hotter object to the colder object until both are at the same temperature (at thermal equilibrium). A chemical change that generates a fire results in products that are very hot. These hot products can transfer heat to colder objects, such as our bodies, or the food in our ovens.

What Takes Place:
The lesson begins with a discussion of what it means to give off heat or to be heated by a fire. Then, students measure the differences in temperature upon dissolving equal amounts of NaCl, $CaCl_2$, and NH_4Cl in 25 mL of water, comparing the temperature of the solution is to the temperature of the water and salt before mixing. The temperature of the solution is higher for $CaCl_2$. However, the temperature of the NaCl and NH_4Cl solutions are lower. Students discuss the meaning of hot and cold, and are introduced to the terms exothermic and endothermic.

Materials: (per class)
- Student worksheet
- 8 100-mL beakers
- 8 thermometers
- room temperature water
- 24 plastic spoons
- 24 beakers for salts (small or medium)
- 8 teaspoon $CaCl_2$ (~24 g)
- 8 teaspoon NaCl (~24 g)
- 8 teaspoon NH_4Cl (~24 g)

Investigation I – Evidence of Change

LESSON 2 – Hot and Cold

In this activity students take a closer look at what it means to be hot or cold. They begin by discussing what we mean when we say a fire warms us. Then students measure the temperature changes that occur upon dissolving three different salts in water. The results are translated onto graphs for easier interpretation and comparison. Students are introduced to the words exothermic and endothermic. They relate the temperature changes they observed to heat transfer either from the solution to the environment or from the environment into the solution.

Exploring the Topic (5–10 min)

1. Introduce the ChemCatalyst exercise.

Write the following exercise on the board for students to complete individually.

Imagine you are sitting near a campfire. You feel warm.

- Explain how you think the burning wood transfers heat to your body.
- The next morning you find ashes that are the same temperature as the air. Explain why the ashes are no longer hot.

2. Discuss the ChemCatalyst exercise.

Use the discussion to get a sense of students' initial ideas.

Discussion goals:

Use the students' written responses to stimulate a discussion about heat transfer.

Sample questions:

Do you think the campfire is at the same temperature as your body? Why or why not?
How do you think heat is transferred from the campfire to your body?
How do you think gases might be involved in the heat transfer?
Why do you think the fire eventually burns out?
Explain why the ashes are no longer hot when you wake up the next morning.

3. Explain the purpose of today's activity.

If you wish you can write the main question on the board.

Points to cover:

Tell students they will explore the meaning of hot and cold by measuring temperature changes that occur upon dissolving three different salts in water.

They will answer the question: "What does it mean to say that something is hot or cold?"

Activity - Hot and Cold (15 min)

4. Introduce the activity. (Worksheet)

Pass out the worksheet and explain the lab activity. Go over safety precautions. Students will work in groups of four.

Safety note: Wear goggles.

Materials (per group of 4 students):
1 100-mL beaker
thermometer
water
3 plastic spoons
1 teaspoon $CaCl_2$ (~3 g)
1 teaspoon NaCl (~3 g)
1 teaspoon NH_4Cl (~3 g)

Procedure:
1. Add 25 mL of water to an empty beaker.
2. Measure the temperature of the water. Record the temperature.
3. Add one level teaspoon of $CaCl_2$, calcium chloride, to the water and stir.
4. Quickly place the thermometer in the solution. Record the highest temperature you observe. Feel the outside of the beaker.
5. Rinse the beaker and thermometer.
6. Repeat the procedure for NaCl, sodium chloride. Be sure to use a clean, dry spoon.
7. Report the procedure for NH_4Cl, ammonium chloride. Be sure to use a clean dry spoon.

	$CaCl_2$	NaCl	NH_4Cl
Initial temperature	**25°C**	**25°C**	**25°C**
Final temperature	**51°C**	**22°C**	**6°C**
Temp. change = final temp. – initial temp	**+26°C**	**–3°C**	**–19°C**

Answer the following questions:
1. The temperature change is written ΔT, pronounced "delta T." You find it by calculating the final temperature minus the initial temperature.

a. What does it mean if $\Delta T > 0$?
b. What does it mean if $\Delta T < 0$?

2. When the temperature of the solution increases, some of the heat energy is transferred *to* the thermometer. A process that gives off heat to the surroundings is called **exothermic.** Which of the three processes that you carried out is/are exothermic?
3. When the temperature of the solution decreases, some of the heat energy is transferred *from* the thermometer. A process that absorbs heat from the surroundings is called **endothermic.** Which of the three processes that you carried out is/are endothermic?
4. Does your body sense the same temperature change as the thermometer? Explain.
5. If the process is endothermic, do you expect the solution will feel hot or cold? Explain.
6. Suppose you left the $CaCl_2$ solution you prepared in the classroom overnight. Will the solution still be hot? Why or why not?
7. You have wood at 25°C. You start a fire.
   a. Is ΔT positive or negative for the wood? Explain.
   b. Is heat energy transferred from the fire to the environment or from the environment to the fire? Explain.
   c. Is a fire an exothermic or endothermic process? Explain.

Making sense:
What does it mean to say that something is hot? What does cold mean?

If you finish early...
Predict the temperature change for dissolving 2 teaspoons of $CaCl_2$ in 25 mL water. Explain your thinking.
Predict the temperature change for dissolving 1 teaspoon of NH_4Cl in 50 mL of water. Explain your thinking.

Making Sense Discussion (10–15 min)

Major goals: The main goal of this discussion is to allow students the opportunity to share their results and observations. Students should come away with the notion that temperature can either increase or decrease when matter is altered. They should also begin to use the words exothermic and endothermic when they refer to temperature changes and the associated transfer of heat. These ideas will be processed in greater detail in the following lesson.

5. Discuss students' observations.

Draw a graph on the board for discussions of temperature change. Fill the blank one out as your discussion proceeds.

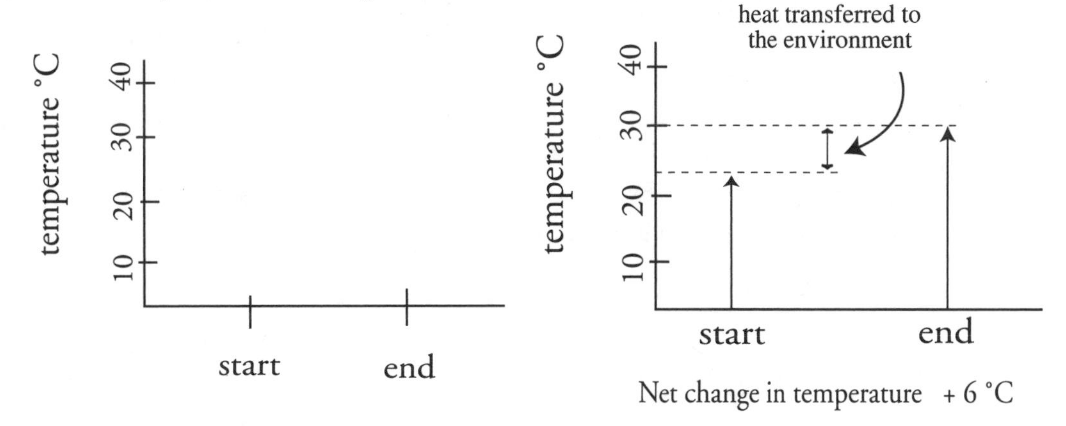

Discussion goals:

Allow students the opportunity to share their observations about hot and cold.

Sample questions:

What kinds of temperature changes did you observe? (one solution got hot and two got cold)

Did your body sense the same temperature change as the thermometer?

How can you explain a sensation of heat in terms of heat transfer?

How can you explain a sensation of cold in terms of heat transfer?

How is the magnitude of ΔT related to the amount of heat transferred?

Imagine the graph represents the results of one of the procedures you completed. Describe what happened.

Points to cover:

Changes in matter are accompanied by a temperature change. In this case, the process of dissolving salts in water led to an increase in temperature for $CaCl_2$, and a decrease in temperature for NaCl and NH_4Cl. Your body senses the same temperature change as the thermometer. When the temperature increases, you sense hot. When the temperature decreases, you sense cold.

6. Introduce exothermic and endothermic reactions.

Write the terms exothermic and endothermic on the board at the appropriate place in the discussion.

Sample questions:

Did the solution transfer heat to the environment during the process shown in the graph? Explain.

Is the process in the graph exothermic or endothermic?

Points to cover:

When there is a temperature increase it is because energy in the form of heat is being transferred to the environment (i.e., the thermometer, your hand) as a result of the change that is taking place. When there is a temperature decrease, it is because heat energy is being transferred from the environment as a result of the change that is taking place. Chemists have specific words to describe each type of change. A process in which heat is transferred to the environment is called an **exothermic process.** A process in which heat is transferred from the environment is called an **endothermic process.**

Exothermic processes are processes in which heat is transferred to the environment. **Endothermic processes** are processes in which heat is transferred from the environment.

7. Discuss the concept of heat.

Discussion goals:

Provide students with the opportunity to express their ideas about heat and heat transfer.

Sample questions:

What does it mean that something is hot?
What does it mean that something is cold?
Heat is always transferred from hot to cold. If you come in contact with an object that is at 0°C, will heat be transferred to or from your body?
When a hot object comes into contact with a cold object, what happens to the temperature of the hot object? the cold object?
If two objects are at the same temperature is there any heat transfer?

Points to cover:

The sensation of heat is due to a temperature difference. Heat is transferred from a region of higher temperature to a region of lower temperature. The transfer stops when the two objects are at the same temperature. Two or more objects in contact with one another are in **thermal equilibrium** when they reach the same temperature.

For example, we sense cold when we touch an object at a lower temperature. We sense hot when we touch an object at a higher temperature than our body. If we hold a hot or cold object long enough, the object and our hand will reach the same temperature.

Heat is the energy that is transferred from one object to another because of a temperature difference. The direction of heat transfer is always from a hotter object to a colder object.

Thermal equilibrium is reached when two or more objects in contact with one another reach the same temperature.

Check-in (5 min)

8. Introduce the Check-in exercise.

Write the following exercise on the board for students to complete individually.

You have water at 25°C. You dissolve ammonium acetate, $NH_4C_2H_4O_2$, in the water and find the temperature decreases to 15°C.

- Is ΔT positive or negative?
- Is heat energy transferring from the solution to the environment or from the environment to the solution?
- Is the process an exothermic or endothermic process?

9. Discuss the Check-in exercise.

Get a sense of the level of understanding by taking a vote, collecting students' work, or asking students to defend their choices.

Discussion goals:

Make sure students understand the relationship between the direction of heat transfer and changes in temperature.

Sample questions:

Does the solution feel hot or cold? Explain.

Is heat transferred from the solution to the environment or from the environment to the solution? Explain.

Is the process exothermic or endothermic? Explain.

10. Wrap-up

Assist the students in summarizing what was learned in the class.

- Heat is transferred as a result of a temperature difference.
- Heat is transferred from hot to cold until the objects in contact with one another are in thermal equilibrium (the same temperature)
- An exothermic process is one in which heat is transferred to the environment.
- An endothermic process is one in which heat is transferred from the environment.

Homework

11. Assign homework.

Use the homework provided with the curriculum or assign your own.

Homework – Investigation I – Lesson 2

1. *The ocean feels hot to the iceberg.* Use the concept of heat transfer to explain what this statement means.
2. Does your body come to thermal equilibrium with the classroom? Why or why not?

Hot and Cold

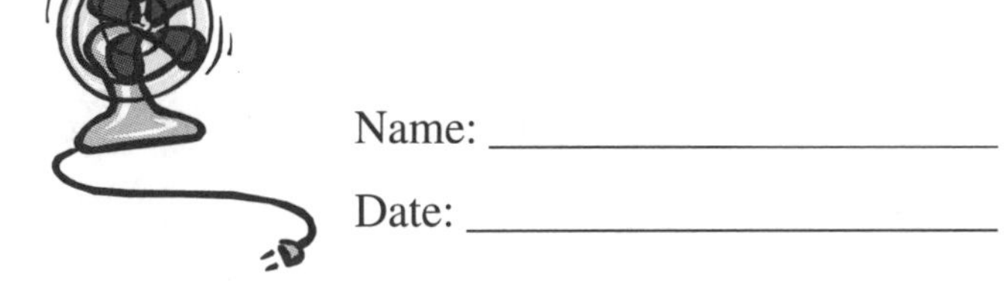

Name: ______________________

Date: ______________________

Student Worksheet

Purpose: The purpose of this lesson is to give you an opportunity to track the energy exchanges that occur when matter is altered.

Procedure:

1. Add 25 mL of water to a 50 mL beaker.
2. Measure the temperature of the water. Record the temperature.
3. Add one level teaspoon of $CaCl_2$, calcium chloride, to the water and stir.
4. Quickly place the thermometer in the solution. Record the highest temperature you observe. Feel the outside of the beaker.
5. Rinse the beaker and thermometer.
6. Repeat the procedure for NaCl, sodium chloride. Be sure to use a clean, dry spoon.
7. Report the procedure for NH_4Cl, ammonium chloride. Be sure to use a clean dry spoon.

	$CaCl_2$	NaCl	NH_4Cl
Initial temperature			
Final temperature			
Temp. change = final temp. – initial temp.			

Answer the following questions:

1. The temperature change is ΔT, pronounced "delta T." You find it by calculating the final temperature minus the initial temperature.
   a. What does it mean if $\Delta T > 0$?

   b. What does it mean if $\Delta T < 0$?

2. When the temperature of the solution increases, some of the heat energy is transferred *to* the thermometer. A process that gives off heat to the surroundings is called **exothermic.** Which of the three processes that you carried out is/are exothermic?

3. When the temperature of the solution decreases, some of the heat energy is transferred *from* the thermometer. A process that absorbs heat from the surroundings is called **endothermic.** Which of the three processes that you carried out is/are endothermic?

4. Does your body sense the same temperature change as the thermometer? Explain.

5. If the process is endothermic, do you expect the solution will feel hot or cold? Explain.

6. Suppose you left the $CaCl_2$ solution you prepared in the classroom overnight. Will the solution still be hot? Why or why not?

7. You have wood at 25°C. You start a fire.
   a. Is ΔT positive or negative for the wood? Explain.

   b. Is heat energy transferred from the fire to the environment or from the environment to the fire? Explain.

   c. Is a fire an exothermic or endothermic process? Explain.

Making sense:
What does it mean to say that something is hot? What does cold mean?

If you finish early...
Predict the temperature change for dissolving 2 teaspoons of $CaCl_2$ in 25 mL water. Explain your thinking.
Predict the temperature change for dissolving 1 teaspoon of NH_4Cl in 50 mL of water. Explain your thinking.

BEFORE CLASS…

LESSON 3 – Point of View

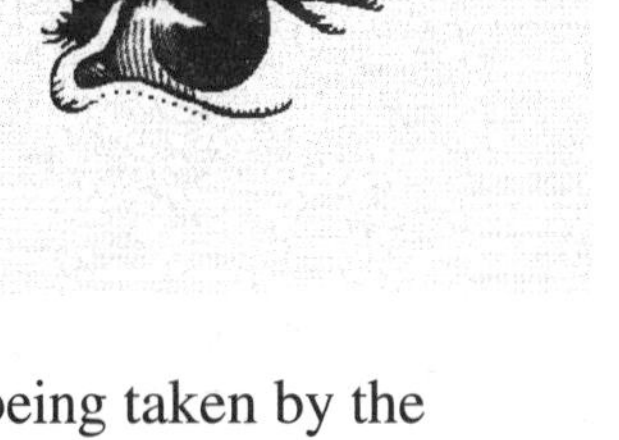

Key Ideas:
Any time there is a change in matter, there is also an energy exchange of some sort. The manner in which energy is experienced and interpreted depends on the point of view that is being taken by the observer. When ice melts in your hand, heat is transferred from the environment (your hand) to the ice. Your hand feels cold as a result. However, there is no such physical thing as "cold," only the loss of heat. The ice is drawing heat from your hand, and is warming as a result. It is important to specify point of view when discussing heat transfer and energy exchanges.

What Takes Place:
Students complete a worksheet working in pairs. They are challenged to look at heat transfer and energy exchanges from different points of view. This lesson focuses on the articulation of students' communications about heat. We want students to realize that what they experience as "hot" and "cold" are really both exchanges of heat, but in opposite directions.

Materials:
- Student worksheet

Investigation I – Evidence of Change

LESSON 3 – Point of View

This activity assists students in looking at the transfer of heat from different points of view. It is easy to become confused about heat transfer unless one specifies the point of view that is being referred to. Students gain practice articulating the relationship between the directionality of heat transfer, what they would observe or experience, and what the system "experiences." The term "system" is introduced to assist students in conceptualizing heat transfer.

Exploring the Topic (10 min)

1. Introduce the ChemCatalyst exercise.

Write the following exercise on the board for students to complete individually.

- Imagine you hold a piece of melting ice in your bare hand. Use the following three words in three different sentences to describe the situation: warm, cold, heat.

2. Discuss the ChemCatalyst exercise.

Use the discussion to get a sense of students' initial ideas. You may wish to have some students write their sentences on the board, or you may wish to write them yourself.

Discussion goals:

Use the students' written responses to stimulate a discussion about experiencing heat transfer.

Sample questions:

Share the sentence you wrote that contains the word "warm."
What is being warmed? What is doing the warming?
Share the sentence you wrote that contains the word "cold."
What is being cooled? What is doing the cooling?
Share the sentence you wrote that contains the word "heat."
What is the meaning of the word "heat" according to your sentence?
Did anyone use the word "heat" in a different manner?
Does your point of view change with your sentences? Explain.
How can we use the words "cold" and "warm" to talk about the same situation?

Below are some examples of the types of sentences that students may offer.

The ice cube feels cold.
My hand is warm compared to the ice cube.
The ice cube makes my hand feel cold.
The heat from my hand is melting the ice cube.

5. Heat is required to boil the water, but the steam feels hot. How can this be?

Making sense:
In any situation with a heat transfer, heat is being absorbed by something and heat is being released by something else. Explain how this applies to cooking soup over a campfire. Include a diagram.

If you finish early...
Cold is a feeling but is not a "thing" that can be transferred from one place to another. Explain what this statement means.

Making Sense Discussion (10–15 min)

Major goals: The main purposes of this discussion are to illuminate the concept of heat transfer further, and to clarify how one's point of view affects communications about heat transfer. The terms "system" and "surroundings" should be defined. Finally, the concept of heat transfer as a way of changing the temperature, and thus, the energy of a system should be explored.

5. Discuss the results of the activity.

You may wish to quickly sketch the fire situations on the board for purposes of discussion. Ask students to come up and place arrows on the illustrations showing the direction of heat transfer.

Discussion goals:
Allow students the opportunity to explain the answers they gave on the worksheet.

Sample questions:
Where did you place your arrows on the five drawings?
What does an arrow represent in these drawings? (the process of heat being transferred in the direction of the arrow)
How did you determine which direction heat was being transferred in each case? (answers will vary)
Does anyone have a different opinion about where the arrows belong on any of the drawings? Explain your thinking.
Would any of the drawings be more accurate with more than one set of arrows? Explain. (The boiling water. Heat is transferred from the combustion of natural gas to the pot and the water. Heat is also transferred from the water vapor to the surrounding air.)

6. Introduce the terms "system" and "surroundings."

Points to cover:
Many times, while exploring chemistry, it becomes necessary to deal with only one part of the universe at a time. We can choose to put our focus on whatever we

want; from a single water molecule, to a beaker of solution, to a campfire, to the atmosphere of an entire planet. The choice of our focus is up to us. However, once a focus has been determined, this chunk of the universe is then referred to as the **system.** The system represents what is being examined or explored. The system can be an object or a process in which matter is being changed.

Once we've defined the system, the rest of the universe is referred to as the **surroundings,** or environment. Everything "outside" the system is considered part of the surroundings. While the system and the surroundings do not overlap with one another, exchange is possible between them. It is possible for matter and energy to pass from the system to the surroundings and vice versa. By defining the system and having a specific focus, we can better keep track of all movements of matter and energy in or out of the system.

Sample questions:

Define the system and the surroundings in the case of the five situations on your worksheet.

Can you define a different system and surroundings in any of the cases? Explain.

What would happen to your explanation of heat transfer if we defined the system as just the aluminum pot, and everything else was the surroundings?

What happens to the arrows when you change the definition of the system?

System: The chunk of the universe being studied (i.e., a water molecule, a beaker of solution, a campfire). **Surroundings:** Everything "outside" the system.

7. Continue the discussion of the definition of heat.

Discussion goals:

Provide students with the opportunity to discuss whether heat is a thing or a process.

Sample questions:

Use the word heat as a noun, in a sentence.

Use the word heat as a verb, in a sentence.

Which sentence makes it sound as if heat is a "thing" or a substance?

Which sentence makes it sound as if heat is an active process?

Are both uses of the word heat correct?

Can you say something *is* cold, or just that it *feels* cold? Why?

Points to cover:

The English language can often be confusing. Sometimes there is a conflict between how a word is used in everyday language and how it is defined scientifically. The word heat is used in more than one way in our language. However, the scientific understanding of heat is very specific. Heat is not a substance or a thing (as the use of heat as a noun would suggest). To a chemist heat is a process. Heat is simply a word that describes an energy transfer. As a result, heat cannot be measured directly, but can only be tracked by making note of changes in temperature. Heat transfer or heat flow is a process by which energy is transferred from one object to another. By noting the temperature change we can measure the energy released (or absorbed) by a system.

We also want students to begin translating from "I'm cold" to "I feel cold" to "I'm losing heat to my environment." There is no such physical thing as "cold," only the loss of heat. For example, the ice is drawing heat from your hand, and is warming as a result. It is all about point of view.

Heat describes the process of energy transfer. Heat is not a "thing" (a noun).

8. Discuss changes in energy due to heat transfer.

Discussion goals:

Provide students with the opportunity to refine their understanding of energy.

Sample questions:

When heat is transferred from an ice cube to the surroundings, how does the ice cube change?

Energy is associated with the degree of motion of the system. How has the degree of motion changed as the ice cube melts? as water boils?

As the temperature increases, does the degree of motion increase or decrease? Explain.

In a fire, the gas molecules in the flame are moving very rapidly. What happens to the motions of these molecules as heat is transferred to the surroundings?

If the temperature rises, does the energy of the system increase or decrease? Explain.

What do you think the concept of equilibrium has to do with the transfer of heat?

Points to cover:

Energy is a property of a system associated with motion and how much work that system can perform. For example, when one car is moving faster than another, we say it has more energy. This becomes more evident if both cars hit an object. The faster moving car will have a greater impact (do more work) than the slower one. In physics, when we examine energy, we are more often concerned with the motion of a large body, like a car. In contrast, in chemistry, when we examine energy, we are more often concerned with the motion of a small particle, like a molecule or an electron. Tracking energy changes due to heat transfer allow us to monitor the motion of small particles.

Heat is a particular type of energy transfer, as a result of atomic and molecular motion. Temperature is a measure of the average kinetic energy (or motion) of a group of particles. When there is a temperature difference between two objects, there is a difference in the motion of the particles of those two objects. At lower temperatures, the energy of a system is lower because the atoms in the system are not moving as fast. Likewise, at higher temperatures, the atoms are moving faster, and therefore, the system has more energy. Heat transfer between a system and the surroundings changes the degree of the motion of the atoms in both. The motion increases in one and decreases in the other, depending on the direction of the transfer. Thus, heat transfer will occur as a natural outcome of the system and surroundings moving towards equilibrium.

We refer to the energy due to motion of the atoms as **internal energy.** Higher internal energy means a greater degree of motion in the atoms. For example, the chemical reaction that produces a fire causes gas molecules to move more rapidly. As heat is transferred to our body from the fire, the rapidly moving gas molecules slow down. And, atoms in our body speed up, and as a result we "feel" warmer.

Energy is a measurement of the capacity of a system to do work or to transfer heat.

Internal energy is associated with the degree of motion of atoms. Heat transfer changes the internal energy of a system.

Check-in (5 min)

9. Introduce the Check-in exercise.

Write the following exercise on the board for students to complete individually.

Imagine a thermometer is placed in a beaker of water and the temperature is noted. An ice cube is dropped into the water and after ten minutes the temperature is noted again.

- Define the system and the surroundings
- What is the direction of heat transfer? Explain.
- How does the internal energy of the system change?

10. Discuss the Check-in exercise.

Get a sense of the level of understanding by taking a vote, collecting students' work, or asking students to defend their choices.

Discussion goals:

Make sure students understand how to articulate the direction of heat transfer.

Sample questions:

Define the system and the surroundings that you used.

What was the direction of heat transfer?

What has happened to the internal energy of the ice cube, water, and thermometer?

11. Wrap-up

Assist the students in summarizing what was learned in the class.

- Heat is a process of energy transfer, and in scientific thought is typically considered a verb.
- A system is defined as the portion of the universe that is being focused on for purposes of tracking the movement of energy and matter.
- The surrounding is that part of the universe outside of a defined system.
- Energy is defined as the measurement of the capacity of a system to do work or to transfer heat.
- Internal energy refers to the degree of motion of the atoms in a system.
- Heat transfer changes the degree of motion of the atoms, and hence the internal energy changes.

Homework

12. Assign homework.

Use the homework provided with the curriculum or assign your own.

Homework - Investigation I - Lesson 2

DAY 1: TITLE, PURPOSE, MATERIALS, PROCEDURE

Pre-lab. Prepare a pre-lab write-up based on the procedure below. Include a Title, Purpose, Materials, and Procedure. In the Procedure section, illustrate the procedure by making a diagram of the equipment set up.

You will work in teams of 8 divided into 4 pairs. The 4 pairs in a team will each examine a different experimental condition.

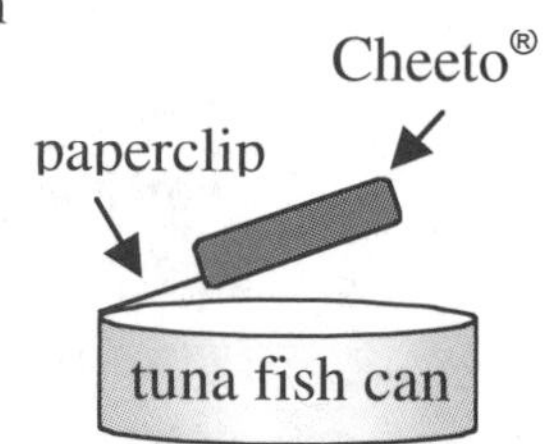

Pair A: Test half a Cheeto® puff with 100 mL of water
Pair B: Test half a Cheeto® puff with 200 mL of water
Pair C: Test a whole Cheeto® puff with 100 mL of water
Pair D: Test a whole Cheeto® puff with 200 mL of water

Procedure:

1. Weigh the Cheeto® you intend to burn. Record the mass in Data Table 1.
2. Create a Cheeto® holder with a paperclip. One end of the paperclip should be pointed at an angle upward as shown in the diagram. Push this end into the Cheeto®. Tape the other end of the paperclip to the side of an empty tuna fish can. Put aluminum foil around the can as a shield as shown in the picture.

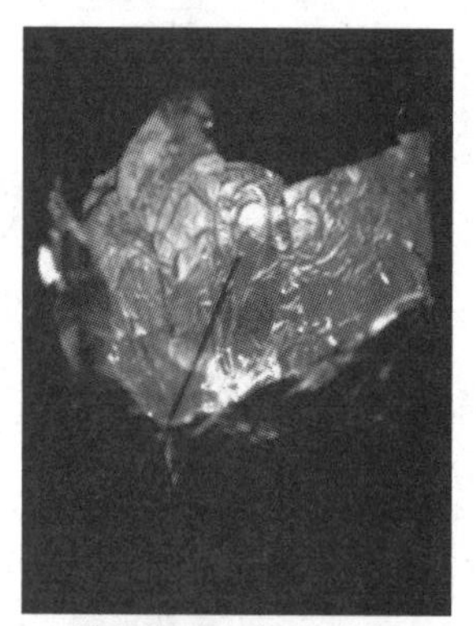

3. Hang a soda can with a paperclip chain from the tab on the soda can to a clamp on the ringstand as shown in the picture. Adjust the height so that the soda can is about 2 inches above the Cheeto®.
4. Fill the soda can with the amount of water you were assigned to heat. Measure the initial temperature (in degrees Celsius) of the water and record the temperature in Data Table 1.
5. Remove the thermometer from the soda can and remove the soda can from the ringstand.

6. Use a match to light the Cheeto® on fire.
7. Once the Cheeto® is on fire, quickly place the soda can with water over the flame. If the flame goes out, relight the Cheeto®.
8. After the Cheeto® has burned as much as possible, gently stir the water in the soda can and measure the final temperature of the water. Record the temperature in Data Table 1.
9. Weigh what remains of the Cheeto®. Record the mass in Data Table 1.

Point of View

Name: ______________________

Period: ____Date: ____________

Purpose: In this lesson you will consider heat transfer from different points of view.

Examine the following diagrams and answer the questions:

Ice Cube Melting on a Counter Top:

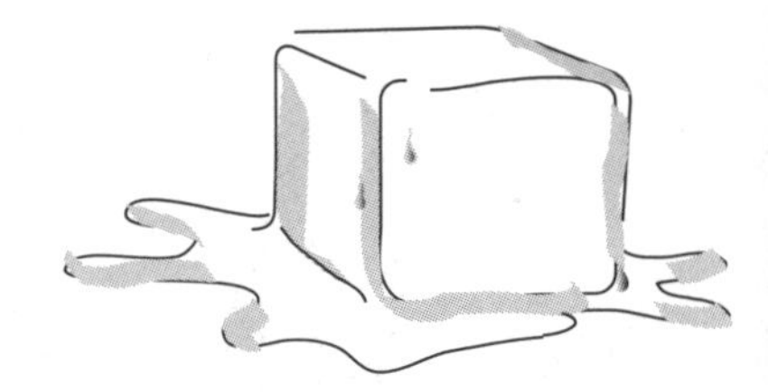

1. Draw arrows showing which direction heat is being transferred, into, or out of, the ice cube.
2. Where exactly is the heat coming from?
3. How are the molecules of H_2O in the puddle of water different from the molecules of water still in the solid ice cube?
4. When the ice cube melts, is it releasing heat or taking heat from the environment?

Water Freezing in an Ice Cube Tray:

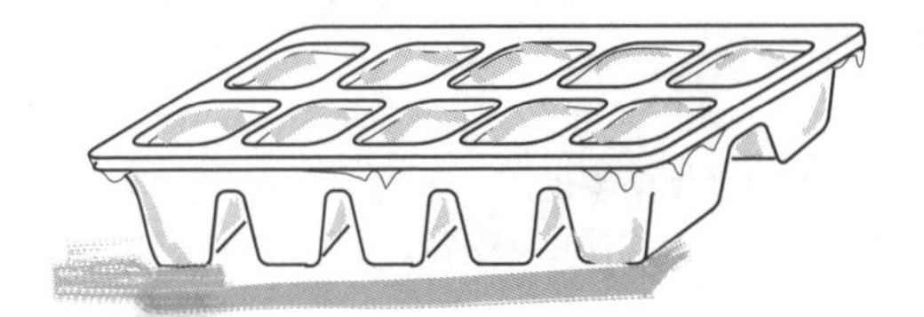

1. Draw arrows showing which direction heat is being transferred when the ice cube tray is placed in the freezer. Is heat being transferred into or out of the water as it freezes into ice?
2. Is heat being transferred into or out of the air directly around the ice cube tray?
3. In order to cool things in a refrigerator, heat must be transferred away from the food. Where do you think this heat ends up going?
4. When the water is freezing, is it releasing heat or taking heat from the environment?

Making an NH_4Cl solution

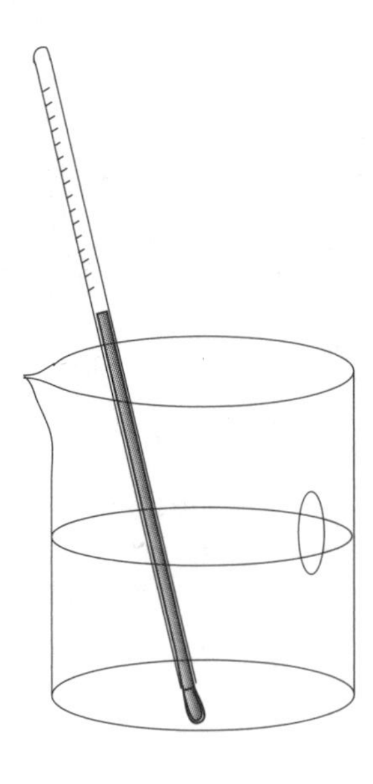

1. The temperature decreases when you prepare a solution of NH_4Cl. Draw arrows showing which direction heat is being transferred just after you prepare the solution. Include the direction of heat transfer between the solution and the thermometer.
2. What does your hand experience if it comes in contact with the solution?
3. Do you think this process would be used to create a cold pack to reduce swelling or a hot pack to increase circulation? Explain.

4. When the NH_4Cl dissolves, heat is absorbed yet the temperature decreases. How can this be?

Match Burning:

1. Draw arrows showing which direction heat is being transferred in the following situation.
2. What is the cause of the heat transfer in this particular situation?
3. Heat is released when a match burns, yet the temperature of the match increases. How can this be?

Boiling Water on the Stove:

1. Draw arrows showing which direction heat is being transferred in the following situation.
2. What is heating the water in the pot?
3. What temperature does the water, H_2O (l), reach? How do you know?
4. What happens to the temperature of the water vapor, H_2O (g), once it leaves the pot and condenses into steam? Explain.
5. Heat is required to boil the water, but the steam feels hot. How can this be?

Making sense:
In any situation with a heat transfer, heat is being absorbed by something and heat is being released by something else. Explain how this applies to cooking soup over a campfire. Include a diagram.

If you finish early...
Cold is a feeling but is not a "thing" that can be transferred from one place to another. Explain what this statement means.

BEFORE CLASS…

LESSON 4 – Now We're Cookin'

Key Ideas:
When a substance such as wood burns, heat is transferred to the surroundings. We can track the heat that is transferred due to a fire by measuring how warm a container of water gets if it is placed directly above the fire. The mass of the reactants that burn and the mass of the water being heated affect how much heat is transferred. Measurements of heat transfer are called calorimetry.

What Takes Place:
Students begin an investigation of heat transfer in more quantitative detail. They burn Cheeto® puffs in this activity. A soda can with water is placed directly above the burning Cheeto. Students measure the temperature rise of the water due to heat transfer. Groups of eight students will do four experiments, with a pair of students in the group doing one of the four. Each pair of students will investigate a different experimental situation in which either the mass of the Cheeto or the mass of the water is changed.

Materials (per class of 32 students):

- Student worksheet
- 1 small bag of Cheeto puffs (at least 16 pieces)
- 16 ring stands with clamps
- 100 paper clips
- 16 empty tuna fish cans
- 16 empty soda cans with tab
- 16 thermometers
- 2 L water
- tape
- 1 roll aluminum foil
- 2–3 boxes of matches

Investigation I – The Nature of Heat

LESSON 4 – Now We're Cookin'

Students continue their exploration of heat transfer by completing a calorimetry experiment involving the heating of water by burning Cheetos. Students will investigate how heat transfer relates to the mass of the Cheeto as well as to the mass of the water being heated. This activity is processed in greater detail in the following lesson.

Exploring the Topic (5 min)

1. Give students a pre-lab quiz.

Use these questions as pre-lab quizzes to make sure your students are prepared.

- How will you determine ΔT in this experiment?
- How will you determine the mass of the Cheeto that burns?
- On your diagram, what is the direction of the heat transfer in this experiment?
- What data will you be collecting in this experiment?
- What are the 2 variables that are being tested in this experiment?

2. Briefly introduce calorimetry.

Points to cover:
One way to measure the amount of heat a substance can transfer when it burns is to burn it directly under a specific quantity of water. The heat is transferred from the burning substance to warm the water. We can measure how much the temperature of the water changes when the substance burns. The measurement of the amount of heat transferred is called **calorimetry.**

In today's experiment, you will burn a Cheeto under a soda can with water and record the temperature change of the water in the soda can. You will examine different masses of Cheeto and different quantities of water.

Calorimetry: The measurement of the amount of heat transferred.

3. Explain the purpose of today's activity.

If you wish you can write the main question on the board.

Points to cover:
One way to measure the amount of heat a substance can transfer when it burns is to burn it underneath water. As the heat is transferred to the water, the temperature rise of the water can be measured. Tell students they will be gathering information to answer the question: "How much does the temperature of water change when you burn something beneath it?"

Activity – Now We're Cookin' (15 min)

4. Introduce the activity. (Worksheet)

Pass out the worksheet and explain the lab activity. Go over safety precautions. Students will work in teams of 8 divided into 4 pairs. The 4 pairs in a team will each examine a different experimental condition.

Safety note: Since students will be using fire today, make sure all students are wearing goggles, have their hair tied back, and are not wearing any loose clothing, especially loose sleeves.

Materials (per pair of students):

1 Cheeto
1 ring stand with clamp
6–7 paper clips
1 empty tuna can
1 soda can with tab
100–200 mL of water
1 thermometer
aluminum foil
matches
tape

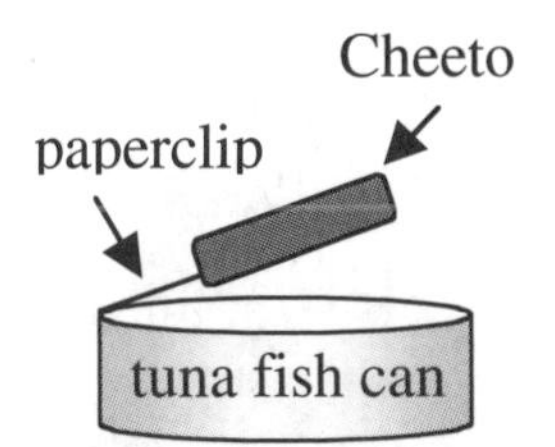

Experimental conditions:

Pair A: Test half a Cheeto with 100 mL of water
Pair B: Test half a Cheeto with 200 mL of water
Pair C: Test a whole Cheeto with 100 mL of water
Pair D: Test a whole Cheeto with 200 mL of water

Procedure:

1. Weigh the Cheeto you intend to burn. Record the mass in Data Table 1.
2. Create a Cheeto holder with a paperclip. One end of the paperclip should be pointed at an angle upward as shown in the diagram. Push this end into the Cheeto. Tape the other end of the paperclip to the side of an empty tuna fish can. Put aluminum foil around the can as a shield as shown in the picture.
3. Hang a soda can with a paperclip chain from the tab on the soda can to a clamp on the ringstand as shown in the picture. Adjust the height so that the soda can is about 2 inches above the Cheeto.
4. Fill the soda can with the amount of water you were assigned to heat. Measure the initial temperature (in degrees Celsius) of the water and record the temperature in Data Table 1.

5. Remove the thermometer from the soda can and remove the soda can from the ringstand.
6. Use a match to light the Cheeto on fire.
7. Once the Cheeto is on fire, quickly place the soda can with water directly over the flame. If the flame goes out, relight the Cheeto.
8. After the Cheeto has burned as much as possible, gently stir the water in the soda can and measure the final temperature of the water. Record the temperature in Data Table 1.

9. Weigh what remains of the Cheeto. Record the mass in Data Table 1.
10. Complete the calculations and record them in Data Table 2. Fill out both Data Tables 1 and 2 with data from the other 3 pairs in your team.

Data Table 1: Data Collection

DATA*						
	Fuel	Initial mass of fuel	Final mass of fuel	mL of water	Initial T of water	Final T of water
A	half of a Cheeto	**0.5 g**	**0.07 g**	100	**25°C**	**33°C**
B	half of a Cheeto	**0.5 g**	**0.07 g**	200	**25°C**	**29°C**
C	whole Cheeto	**1.0 g**	**0.15 g**	100	**25°C**	**39°C**
D	whole Cheeto	**1.0 g**	**0.15 g**	200	**25°C**	**33°C**

* Masses and temperatures will vary depending on the experimental set-up.

Data Table 2: Calculations

CALCULATIONS				
	Heat Source	Grams of water	Change in Temp = Final T – Initial T	Mass of fuel burned = Initial Mass – Final Mass
A	half of a Cheeto	100 g	**8°C**	**0.43 g**

B	half of a Cheeto	200 g	**4°C**	**0.43 g**
C	whole Cheeto	100 g	**14°C**	**0.85 g**
D	whole Cheeto	200 g	**8°C**	**0.85 g**

Answer the following questions:

1. What happened to the temperature change of the water when you doubled the mass of Cheeto you used?
2. What happened to the temperature change of the water when you doubled the amount of water that was heated?

Making sense:
What conclusions can you draw based on your experimental results?

If you finish early...
When you burned your Cheeto it decreased in mass. What happened to the mass that was lost? Where did it go?

Making Sense Discussion (10–15 min)

Major goals: Due to the length of the lab this discussion should be brief. The four experimental conditions should be compared in order to determine the effects of doubling the amount of fuel and the amount of water. The data will be analyzed in greater detail in tomorrow's class.

5. Collect class data.

Put Data Table 3 on the board. Ask the group that finishes first to fill out Data Table 3 on the board for the discussion.

Data Table 3: Change in Temperature

Fuel	Grams of water	Change in Temperature*
half Cheeto	100 g	**8°C**
half Cheeto	200 g	**4°C**
whole Cheeto	100 g	**14°C**
whole Cheeto	200 g	**8°C**

*Changes in temperature will vary depending on the experimental set-up.

Discussion goals:

Discuss how the temperature rise for the water is affected by the mass of the Cheeto and the amount of water.

Sample questions:

Is the burning of the Cheeto an exothermic or endothermic reaction?
Why does the temperature of the water rise?
Is all the heat transferred to the water? Explain your answer.
What happens to the temperature of the water when you increase the mass of Cheeto?
What happens to the temperature of the water when you increase the amount of water?

Points to cover:

In this experiment, students burned Cheetos to warm water. The temperature rise of the water depended both on the mass of the Cheeto and on the amount of water. Point out that the chemical change of the Cheeto burning transfers heat to cause the physical change of increasing the temperature of the water.

When the mass of Cheeto is increased, more heat is transferred to the water. When the amount of water is increased, more heat is required to raise the temperature. Tell students that in tomorrow's lesson, they will investigate this lab more extensively and quantify the amount of heat transferred from the burning of the Cheeto.

You should also point out that there are experimental errors associated with this measurement. Some of the heat transferred warms the soda can and some warms the surrounding air. Thus, the measurement of the temperature of the water only provides a lower limit on the total amount of heat transferred.

Check-in (5 min)

6. No Check-in for this class.

7. Wrap-up

Assist the students in summarizing what was learned in the class.

- Calorimetry is the measurement of the amount of heat transferred.
- The temperature rise of water is a measure of the amount of heat transferred from a chemical change such as a fire.

Homework

8. Assign homework.

Use the homework provided with the curriculum or assign your own.

Homework – Investigation I – Lesson 4

DAY 2: DATA AND OBSERVATIONS

Add Data and Observations to the laboratory write-up you began yesterday in preparation for the experiment you did in class today.

Observations: Draw a diagram of your calorimetry experiment.

1. Draw arrows showing which direction heat is being transferred in your calorimetry experiment. Include arrows showing which direction heat is being transferred into or out of the water and into or out of the pellet.
2. What is heating the water in the soda can?
3. Is heat required or released by the Cheeto? Explain your reasoning.
4. Is heat required or released by the water? Explain your reasoning.
5. Heat is required to raise the temperature of the water, but the burning Cheeto feels hot. How can that be? Explain your reasoning.
6. What is the system and what are the surroundings?

Data: Include your team's data and calculations in your lab-write up. Use the table format from the activity.

1. What happened to the temperature change of the water when you doubled the amount of fuel you used?
2. What happened to the temperature change of the water when you doubled the amount of water that was heated?

Student Worksheet

Now We're Cookin'

Name: ______________________

Period: ______ Date: __________

Purpose: You will measure the amount of heat released from burning a Cheeto by measuring the temperature rise of water. You will examine 4 different conditions.

Safety note: You will be using fire today. Make sure you wear goggles. Tie your hair back. Do not wear loose clothing, especially loose sleeves.

Materials (per pair of students):

1 Cheeto
1 ring stand with clamp
6–7 paper clips
1 empty tuna fish can
1 soda can with tab

100–200 mL of water
1 thermometer
aluminum foil
matches
tape

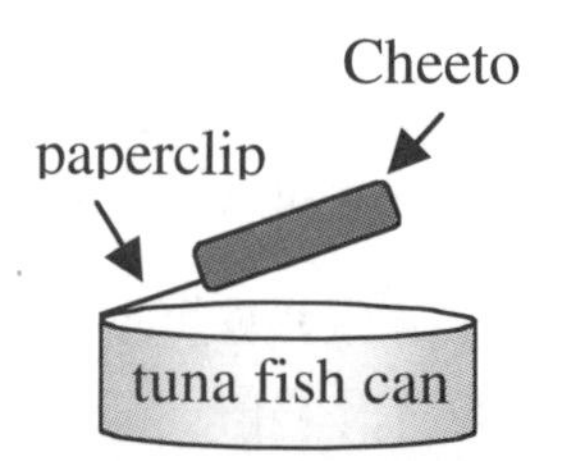

Experimental conditions:

You will work in a team of 8 divided into 4 pairs. The 4 pairs in a team will each examine a different experimental condition.

Pair A: Test half a Cheeto with 100 mL of water
Pair B: Test half a Cheeto with 200 mL of water
Pair C: Test a whole Cheeto with 100 mL of water
Pair D: Test a whole Cheeto with 200 mL of water

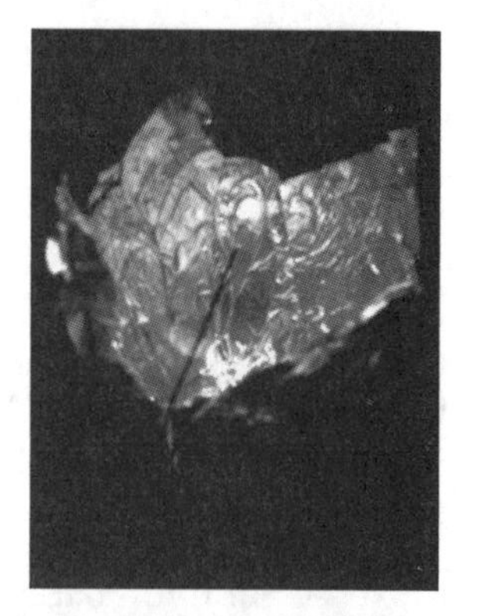

Procedure:

1. Weigh the Cheeto you intend to burn. Record the mass in Data Table 1.
2. Create a Cheeto holder with a paperclip. One end of the paperclip should be pointed at an angle upward as shown in the diagram. Push this end into the Cheeto. Tape the other end of the paperclip to the side of an empty tuna fish can. Put aluminum foil around the soda can as a shield as shown in the picture.
3. Hang a soda can with a paperclip chain from the tab on the soda can to a clamp on the ringstand as shown in the picture. Adjust the height so that the can is about 2 inches above the Cheeto.
4. Fill the soda can with the amount of water you were assigned to heat. Measure the initial temperature (in degrees Celsius) of the water and record the temperature in Data Table 1.
5. Remove the thermometer from the soda can and remove the soda can from the ringstand.
6. Use a match to light the Cheeto on fire.
7. Once the Cheeto is on fire, quickly place the soda can with water directly over the flame. If the flame goes out, relight the Cheeto.
8. After the Cheeto has burned as much as possible, gently stir the water in the soda can and measure the final temperature of the water. Record the temperature in Data Table 1.
9. Weigh what remains of the Cheeto. Record the mass in Data Table 1.
10. Complete the calculations and record them in Data Table 2. Fill out both Data Tables 1 and 2 with data from the other 3 pairs in your team.

Data Table 1: Data Collection

DATA*						
	Fuel	Initial mass of fuel	Final mass of fuel	mL of water	Initial T of water	Final T of water
A	half of a Cheeto			100		
B	half of a Cheeto			200		
C	whole Cheeto			100		
D	whole Cheeto			200		

*Masses and temperatures will vary depending on the experimental set-up.

Data Table 2: Calculations

CALCULATIONS				
	Heat Source	Grams of water	Change in Temp = Final T – Initial T	Mass of fuel burned = Initial Mass – Final Mass
A	half of a Cheeto	100 g		
B	half of a Cheeto	200 g		
C	whole Cheeto	100 g		
D	whole Cheeto	200 g		

Answer the following questions:

1. What happened to the temperature change of the water when you doubled the mass of Cheeto you used?

2. What happened to the temperature change of the water when you doubled the amount of water that was heated?

Making sense:
What conclusions can you draw based on your experimental results?

If you finish early...
When you burned your pellets they decreased in mass. What happened to the mass that was lost? Where did it go?

BEFORE CLASS…

LESSON 5 – Fat Calories

Key Ideas:

A calorie is defined as the amount of heat needed to raise the temperature of 1 gram of water by 1 degree centigrade. If we burn a substance directly below a container of water, we can quantify the amount of heat transferred per gram of substance burned. The number of calories transferred to the water is related to the mass of the water and the temperature change. The number of calories transferred from the substance that burns depends on the identity of the substance and its mass.

What Takes Place:

Students begin the lesson by sketching the calorimetry experiment they did in the previous lesson. They use arrows to show the direction of heat transfer. This leads to the definition of a calorie as a measure of the amount of heat transferred. Students use this definition to determine the calorie content of a Cheeto® puff. (They use data similar to the data they collected.) The measured calorie content is compared with the food calories reported on the Cheetos bag. Students discuss how digestion of Cheetos transfers heat to our bodies to keep us warm. For homework, students complete the analysis of the data their team collected for 4 different sets of experimental conditions in yesterday's lesson.

Materials:

- Student worksheets

Investigation I – Evidence of Change

LESSON 5 – Fat Calories

In this lesson, students analyze further the data they obtained in yesterday's experiment. The calorie is introduced as a measure of heat. Students use the definition of a calorie to analyze the heat transfer in the calorimetry experiment. The calories absorbed by the water depend on the specific heat capacity of water, the mass of water heated, and the magnitude of the temperature change. The burning Cheeto released the calories absorbed by the water. The lesson ends with a discussion of food Calories and how they are determined.

Exploring the Topic (5–10 min)

1. Introduce the ChemCatalyst exercise.

Write the following exercise on the board for students to complete individually.

- Draw a diagram of the calorimetry experiment you did yesterday.
- Use arrows to show if heat is being transferred into or out of the Cheeto.
- Use arrows to show if heat is being transferred into or out of the water.

2. Discuss the ChemCatalyst exercise.

Use the discussion to get a sense of students' initial ideas.

Discussion goals:

Use the students' written responses to stimulate an open-ended discussion about the transfer of heat in the calorimetry experiment.

Sample questions:

In which direction is heat being transferred?

Why does the temperature of the water increase?

Is heat required or released by the water? Explain your reasoning.

Is heat required or released by the Cheeto? Explain your reasoning.

Heat is transferred from a region of higher temperature to a region of lower temperature. Is this happening in the Cheeto experiment?

What evidence do you have that the Cheeto is releasing heat? Does the temperature of the Cheeto go up or down?

Discuss the following statement: If you know the heat needed to raise the temperature of the water, then you know the heat released by the burning Cheeto.

Give the students the opportunity to discuss how the heat is transferred from the burning Cheeto to the water. The water absorbs heat. We know this because the temperature rises. The burning Cheeto releases heat. This is a bit confusing because the Cheeto is hot. But, of course, over time, the flame goes out and the remains of the Cheeto cool down.

3. Introduce the calorie.

Points to cover:
A **calorie** is a unit of heat measurement. A calorie is defined as the amount of heat needed to raise the temperature of 1 gram of water by 1 degree Celsius. In other words, if the temperature of 1 gram of water increases by 1 degree Celsius, then 1 calorie of heat has been transferred to the water. If we know the mass of water and the change in temperature, then we know the number of calories.

The ratio of 1 calorie / (1gram • 1°C) is called the **specific heat capacity of water.** It is the conversion factor to go between calories, grams, and temperature change.

$$\text{specific heat capacity of water} = \frac{1 \text{ calorie}}{1\text{gram} \bullet 1 \text{ degree}} = 1\frac{\text{cal}}{\text{g } \Delta\text{T}}$$

Sample questions:
How many calories do you need to raise the temperature of 1 g of water by 2°C?
How many calories do you need to raise the temperature of 2 g of water by 1°C?
How many calories do you need to raise the temperature of 2 g of water by 2°C?

Calorie: The amount of heat needed to raise the temperature of one gram of water by one degree Celsius.

Specific heat capacity of water is the conversion factor between calories, grams, and temperature change. For water, the conversion factor is 1 calorie/(1 gram • 1°C).

4. Explain the purpose of today's activity.

If you wish you can write the main question on the board.

Points to cover:
Tell students that in today's activity they will be quantifying the amount of heat transferred from a system such as burning Cheetos to water. They will be answering the question: "How many calories of heat are transferred from the burning Cheeto to the water?"

Activity – Fat Calories (15 min)

5. Introduce the activity. (Worksheet)

Pass out the worksheet. Ask students to work with a partner.

Answer the following questions:

1. Suppose you heat 150 mL of water. The temperature of the water changes from 20°C to 32°C.

CALORIES TRANSFERRED TO WATER					
volume	grams	initial T	final T	ΔT	calories
150 mL	**150 g**	20°C	32°C	**12°C**	**1800 cal**

Answer these questions as you complete the table above.

a. How do you calculate the mass of the water if you just have the volume? (Hint: What is the density of water?) (use 1 g/mL conversion factor)

b. How do you calculate ΔT? (final T – initial T)

c. How do you calculate the number of calories transferred to the water?

$$\text{specific heat capacity of water} = 1\frac{\text{cal}}{\text{g }\Delta\text{T}}$$

Rewrite the equation so you can solve for the number of calories needed to raise the temperature of 150 mL of water by 12°C. (Ans.: 1800 cal)

x cal = (specific heat capacity) (mass) (temperature change)

$$x = \frac{1\text{ cal}}{1\text{g} \bullet 1°\text{C}} (150\text{ g})(12°\text{C}) = \boxed{}$$

2. Suppose you heated the water in Question 1 by burning 1.1 g of Cheeto. When the fire went out, the final mass of the Cheeto was 0.15 g.

CALORIES TRANSFERRED FROM THE CHEETO				
initial mass	final mass	mass that burned	total calories transferred to the water	calories per gram Cheeto
1.1 g	0.15 g	**0.95 g**	**1800 cal**	**1895 cal/g**

a. How do calculate the mass of Cheeto that burned?

b. How do you calculate the total calories transferred to the water? (Hint: See Question 1.)

c. How do you calculate the calories per gram of Cheeto?

(1800 cal / 0.95 g = 1895 cal / g)

3. The nutrition facts for Cheetos are given in the chart.

   a. We often speak of the calories associated with food. What do you think this means?

   b. Eating food helps to keep us warm. How might this happen?

   c. How many food Calories are in 1 Cheeto? Use the information in the chart. (5.5 food Calories)

   d. Food Calories are 1000 times greater than the calories used by chemists. How many chemistry calories are in 1 Cheeto? (5500 calories)

   e. How does this number compare with the cal/g you calculated in Question 2? (it is bigger)

   f. Why do you think the measured value is lower than the value reported on the Cheeto bag? (our experimental set-up could be improved – the heat was not transferred perfectly to the water)

   g. How do you think the Calories reported on the bag of Cheetos are measured? (perhaps in a similar way)

Calories in Cheetos® **Nutrition Facts**
Serving Size: 1 oz (~29 g) ~29 pieces
Calories 160
Calories from Fat 90
Total Fat 10 g
Total Carbohydrates 15 g
Protein 2 g
Other: 2 g

Making Sense:
What do you need to know to quantify the amount of heat transferred from a fire to a container of water? List the 3 pieces of data you need to collect.

If you finish early...
If you burn a larger number of Cheetos you can heat the water up to a higher temperature. However, the temperature of the fire itself does not change with the number of Cheetos you use. Explain what might be going on.

Making Sense Discussion (10–15 min)

Major goals: One of the main goals of this lesson is to provide students with an understanding of how to quantify heat transfer. Students should come away from the lesson with the idea that the heat transferred when a substance burns can be quantified by warming water. In addition, the discussion makes a link between the calories given on the nutrition information labels on food and the calories measured by burning food under a container of water in a calorimetry experiment.

6. Elaborate on the meaning of calories

Discussion goals:

Discuss the relationship between the "calorie content" of a fuel and the calories needed to warm water.

Sample questions:

What do you need to know to quantify the number of calories needed to warm water (specific heat capacity, mass of water, temperature change)?

What do we mean when we say that a substance has a certain number of calories per gram?

We often say that a substance "contains calories." This is not really correct. Explain why.

If a substance burns, we say it transfers a certain number of calories per gram. What do we mean by this?

Points to cover:

When we transfer heat to a container of water, the temperature of the water increases. The calories transferred to the water can be determined by measuring the amount of water and the temperature change. One calorie is absorbed to heat 1 g of water by 1°C. We know this ratio from the specific heat capacity of water. Indeed, this is how the measurement of heat is defined.

The calories needed to warm the water are transferred due to contact with a substance that is at a higher temperature than the water. A common way to transfer heat is to create a fire with a substance that burns. We refer to substances that burn as **fuels.** Fuels react with oxygen causing the system to get hotter than the surroundings. Each fuel can be labeled with a certain number of calories per gram. This does not mean that the fuel "contains" calories. Rather, it means that if you burn 1 gram of the fuel, you will know how much heat can be transferred.

Fuels are substances such as wood and food, which react with oxygen to transfer heat.

7. Discuss what we mean by food Calories.

Discussion goals:

Help students to relate food Calories with their experience burning Cheetos.

Sample questions:

What do we mean when we say that food has Calories?

How do you think the Calorie content of food is measured?

The calories per gram determined by the burning Cheeto experiment is less than half the amount reported on the Cheeto bag. Explain why the experimental value is low? What are the experimental errors?

What do you think it might mean if we say that digestion of food is a "slow burn"?

In terms of what we have been discussing, what does it mean that we eat food to keep us warm?

Points to cover:

When we say that food has Calories, we mean that when we burn the food, it will transfer a certain amount of heat. Now, of course, food is not "burning" in our stomachs. However, we do breathe in oxygen, which reacts with the food to slowly transfer heat to our bodies as the food digests. In the same way, oxygen is needed to react with substances that produce fire. In a sense, digestion is a "slow burn."

The **food Calories** given on the labels of packages of food refer to the amount of heat transferred when the food is burned. The idea is the same as burning a Cheeto as we did in yesterday's experiment, but the unit is 1000 times greater than the calories used by chemists. Hence, we give food Calories a capital C to remind us that they are larger.

The value measured in the Cheeto burning experiment is less than half of the value reported on the Cheeto bag. This is due to experimental error. Not all of the heat from the burning Cheeto was transferred to the water. Some of the heat was transferred to the soda can and to the surrounding air.

Food Calories measure the heat released when food is burned. Food Calories are 1000 times larger than the calories used by chemists.

8. Go over a calculation of number of calories.

Discussion goals:

Discuss how to determine the calories per gram of a cashew.

You burn 1 cashew, which weighs 3.5 g. The cashew burns completely so that there is no solid left once the flame extinguishes. The temperature of 400 mL of water increases by 35°C. Determine the calories per gram of cashew. Explain the value reported on the nutrition label.

Calories in Cashews Nutrition Facts
Serving Size: 1 oz (28.3 g) ~8 pieces
Calories 160
Calories from Fat 120
Total Fat 13.3 g
Total Carbohydrates 7.7 g
Protein 5.2 g
Other: 2.1 g

Solution

Step 1: Determine the number of calories of heat transferred to the water.

$$\text{specific heat capacity of water} = 1\frac{\text{cal}}{\text{g}\ \Delta\text{T}}$$

1 calorie is needed to raise the temperature of 1 gram of water by 1°C. So if you have 400 g of water and the temperature raises 1°C, 400 cal of heat was transferred to the water.

$$x \text{ cal} = (\text{specific heat capacity})\ (\text{mass})\ (\text{temperature change})$$

$$= \frac{1 \text{ cal}}{1\text{g} \bullet 1°\text{C}}\ (400 \text{ g})\ (1°\text{C}) = 400 \text{ cal}$$

If you have just 1 g of water and the temperature rises 35°C then the calorie change is 35 cal.

$$x \text{ cal} = \frac{1 \text{ cal}}{1\text{g} \bullet 1°\text{C}}\ (1 \text{ g})\ (35°\text{C}) = 35 \text{ cal}$$

In this problem, you need to calculate the number of calories needed to raise the temperature of 400 mL of water by 35°C.

$$? \text{ cal} = \frac{1 \text{ cal}}{1\text{g} \bullet 1°\text{C}}\ (400 \text{ g})\ (35°\text{C}) = 14{,}000 \text{ cal}$$

Step 2: The total amount of heat transferred due to burning the cashew is 14,000 cal. The calories per gram can be determined by dividing by the number of grams of cashew.

$$\text{number of calories per gram} = \frac{14{,}000 \text{ cal}}{3.5 \text{ g}} = 4000 \text{ cal/g}$$

Comparison: food calories are 1000 times smaller. We found 14,000 cal/cashew. This is equivalent to 14 food calories/cashew. The nutrition label indicates 160 calories for ~8 cashews or 20 food calories per cashew. The experimental number determined by burning a cashew is smaller presumably due to experimental error.

Check-in (5 min)

9. Introduce the Check-in exercise.

Write the following exercise on the board for students to complete individually.

You burn an 8 g marshmallow to warm 400 mL of water. The temperature of the water increases by 60°C.

- Use the data to show that the 8 g marshmallow has 24000 calories.
- Use the data to show that marshmallows have 3000 cal/g.
- Explain why the label on the bag says that the marshmallow has 24 food Calories per marshmallow.

10. Discuss the Check-in exercise.

Get a sense of the level of understanding by taking a vote, collecting students' work, or asking students to defend their choices.

Discussion goals:

Assess that students understand how to quantify heat transfer.

Sample questions:

How do you measure the amount of heat transferred?

What does the specific heat of water tell you?

What is the relationship between heat transfer, mass of water, and temperature change?

What is the difference between the calories chemists used and food calories on nutrition labels?

11. Wrap-up

Assist the students in summarizing what was learned in the class.

- Heat is measured in calories. It is determined by multiplying the specific heat capacity times the mass times the temperature change.

Homework

12. Assign homework.

Use the homework provided with the curriculum or assign your own.

Students will be completing their lab write-up. Remind teams to exchange phone numbers or e-mail because they need each other's data to complete the lab write-up.

Homework – Investigation I – Lesson 5

DAY 3: CALCULATIONS AND CONCLUSIONS

Add Calculations and Conclusions to the laboratory write-up you began two days ago for the experiment you did in class yesterday. (See homework for Lessons I-3 and I-4)

This is a formal lab report so be sure you have the following sections in your write-up.

I. Title
II. Purpose
III. Materials
IV. Procedure (illustration)
V. Observations
VI. Data
VII. Calculations
VIII. Conclusions

Calculations: Complete your lab write-up. Answer the following questions about the Cheeto burning experiment. You will need the data you collected as well as the data and calculations from the other 3 pairs in your team to determine the number of calories of heat transferred per gram of Cheeto.

1. Fill in the table.

	Grams of water	Δ T	Calories transferred to water	Mass of Cheeto burned	Calories per gram Cheeto (cal/g)
A half Cheeto + 100 mL H_2O					
B half Cheeto + 200 mL H_2O					
C whole Cheeto + 100mL H_2O					
D whole Cheeto + 200mL H_2O					

2. How do the data depend on the mass of the Cheeto?
3. How do the data depend on the mass of the water?

Conclusion: How many calories are released per gram of Cheeto?

Student Worksheet

Fat Calories

Name ______________________

Period ______ Date __________

Purpose: To quantify the number of calories of heat transferred from the burning Cheeto® to the water.

1. Suppose you have 150 mL of water. The temperature of the water changes from 20°C to 32°C.

CALORIES TRANSFERRED TO WATER					
volume	grams	initial T	final T	ΔT	calories
150 mL		20°C	32°C		

Answer these questions as you complete the table above.

a. How do you calculate the mass of the water if you just have the volume? (Hint: What is the density of water?)

b. How do you calculate ΔT?

c. How do you calculate the number of calories transferred to the water?

$$\text{specific heat capacity of water} = 1\frac{\text{cal}}{\text{g}\ \Delta\text{T}}$$

Rewrite the equation so you can solve for the number of calories needed to raise the temperature of 150 mL of water by 12°C.

x cal = (specific heat capacity) (mass) (temperature change)

$$x = \frac{1\ \text{cal}}{1\text{g} \bullet 1°\text{C}}\ (150\ \text{g})\ (12°\text{C}) = \boxed{}$$

2. Suppose you heated the water in Question 1 by burning 1.1 g of Cheeto. When the fire went out, the final mass of the Cheeto was 0.15 g.

CALORIES TRANSFERRED FROM THE CHEETO				
initial mass	final mass	mass that burned	total calories transferred to the water	calories per gram Cheeto
1.1 g	0.15 g			

a. How do you calculate the mass of Cheeto that burned?

b. How do you calculate the total calories transferred to the water? (Hint: See Question 1)

c. How do you calculate the calories per gram of Cheeto?

3. The nutrition facts for Cheetos are given in the chart.

Calories in Cheetos® Nutrition Facts
Serving Size: 1 oz (~29 g) ~29 pieces
Calories 160 Calories from Fat 90
Total Fat 10 g Total Carbohydrates 15 g Protein 2 g Other: 2 g

   a. We often speak of the calories associated with food. What do you think this means?

   b. Eating food helps to keep us warm. How might this happen?

   c. How many food calories are in 1 Cheeto? Use the information in the chart.

   d. Food calories are 1000 times greater than the calories used by chemists. How many chemistry calories are in 1 Cheeto?

   e. How does this number compare with the calories/g you calculated in Question 2?

   f. Why do you think the measured value is lower than the value reported on the Cheetos bag?

   g. How do you think the calories reported on the bag of Cheetos are measured?

Making Sense:
What do you need to know to quantify the amount of heat transferred from a fire to a container of water? List the 3 pieces of data you need to collect.

If you finish early...
If you burn a larger number of Cheetos you can heat the water up to a higher temperature. However, the temperature of the fire itself does not change with the number of Cheetos you use. Explain what might be going on.

BEFORE CLASS…

LESSON 6 – Burning Questions

Key Ideas:

Heat and temperature are not the same. When heat is transferred to a substance, the temperature rises more for a substance with a higher specific heat capacity. When heat is transferred to a substance undergoing a phase change, the temperature does not change. Students saw evidence of this with the heating curve of water in the *Weather* unit. Heat is a measure of the total motion of the atoms in a substance. Temperature is a measure of the average motion. These concepts were also previewed in the *Weather* unit.

What Takes Place:

Students solve problems involving heat transfer. The problems include heating substances other than water, with smaller specific heat capacities. This leads to a discussion about the differences in the amount of heat required to raise the temperature of different substances by the same amount. Students also examine the heat required for phase change. Although heat is transferred, the temperature does not change when a substance changes phase. The lesson ends with a discussion of the difference between heat and temperature in terms of the motions of atoms.

Materials:

- Student worksheets
- 1 sheet poster paper or butcher paper for fire concept map

Investigation I – Evidence of Change

LESSON 6 – Burning Questions

In this lesson, students practice solving problems involving heat transfer. The problems include heating substances other than water and the heat required for phase changes. Specific heat capacities for various substances are compared, and the heat associated with phase changes (latent heat) is introduced. As various substances, amounts, and temperature changes are examined, the focus becomes understanding the difference between heat and temperature in terms of the motions of atoms. The lesson ends with a summary of the *Fire* unit thus far.

Exploring the Topic (5–10 min)

1. Introduce the ChemCatalyst exercise.

Write the following exercise on the board for students to complete individually.

- While you are stranded on a desert island, you need to decide how big a fire to build for different purposes. Which of the following requires the largest fire?
  - (A) Heating 1 liter of water from 25°C to 35°C for washing your hands and face
  - (B) Heating 1 liter of water from 25°C to 100°C to boil water for cooking noodles.
  - (C) Heating 500 liters of water from 25°C to 35°C for taking a bath.
- Explain your thinking.

2. Discuss the ChemCatalyst exercise.

Use the discussion to get a sense of students' initial ideas.

Discussion goals:

Use the students' written responses to stimulate an open-ended discussion about the amount of heat required for raising the temperature of different quantities of water.

Sample questions:

How does the amount of heat you need depend on how hot you want the water? Explain your thinking.

How does the internal energy of the water change as it is heated?

How do you think about the differences between hot and cold water in terms of the motions of the water molecules?

How does the amount of heat you need depend on the amount of water you want to heat? Explain your thinking.

Explain why it takes more heat to raise the temperature of a larger quantity of water in terms of the motions of water molecules.

The ChemCatalyst should cause a bit of a debate. The least amount of heat is needed for heating 1 liter of water from 25°C to 35°C. Some students will think that the amount of heat required is greater if we want to raise the temperature of the water to a higher value (B). However, students may think about how much longer it takes to boil a large pot of water compared with a small pot, and realize that the amount of water also matters. Thus, (C) might require more heat that (B).

3. Explain the purpose of today's activity.

If you wish you can write the main question on the board.

Points to cover:
Tell students that in today's activity they will practice solving problems involving heat transfer. The problems will include heating substances other than water and the heat required for phase changes. As various substances, amounts, and temperature changes are examined, the focus becomes answering the following question: "What is the difference between heat and temperature?" COOL!

Activity – Burning Questions (15 min)

4. Introduce the activity. (Worksheet)

Pass out the worksheet. Ask students to work with a partner.

Answer the following questions:

Challenge: In this activity, you will determine the heat required to raise the temperature of the following substances to 40°C. The different substances are heated over a fire using wood as fuel.

1. Use your experience with heating things to make predictions. Rank the following substances from (1–5) with 5 requiring the most heat to raise the temperature to 40°C.

Substance	**Rank (1** least to **5** most)
30 g of water starting at 20°C	
300 g of water starting at 20°C	
30 g of water starting at 0°C	
30 g of ice starting at 0°C	
30 g aluminum pot starting at 20°C	

2. Explain your thinking.
3. Fill in the table.

CALORIES NEEDED TO RAISE THE TEMPERATURE TO 40°C							
	substance	amount	initial T	Δ T	heat needed to change phase	specific heat capacities	calories required
A	H_2O (l)	30 g	20°C	20°C	0	1 cal/g°C	600 cal
B	H_2O (l)	300 g	20°C	**20°C**	0	1 cal/g°C	**6000 cal**
C	H_2O (l)	30 g	0°C	40°C	0	**1 cal/g°C**	1200 cal
D	H_2O (s)	30 g	0°C	**40°C**	80 cal/g	1 cal/g°C	3600 cal
E	Al (s)	30 g	20°C	**20°C**	0	0.22 cal/g°C	132 cal
F	Al (s)	300 g	20°C	**20°C**	0	0.22 cal/g°C	**1320 cal**

4. Your friend says, "It should take more heat to raise the temperature of 30 g of water from 0°C to 40°C compared with raising the temperature of 30 g of water or even 300 g water by 20 °C because 40ºC is a bigger change. A bigger change in temperature means more heat is needed."

   a. Your friend's conclusion is incorrect. What other factor must be considered? (mass)

   b. Compare A and B. In terms of motions of water molecules, explain why it takes more wood to raise the temperature of a larger quantity of water by the same amount. (More heat is required to raise the internal energy because the motion of a greater number of water molecules needs to be increased.)

   c. Compare A and C. In terms of the motions of the water molecules, explain why it takes more wood to raise the temperature of the same quantity of water by a larger amount. (More heat is required to raise the internal energy because the change in the motion of the molecules is greater.)

5. When you boil water in an aluminum pot on the stove, the pot gets hot much faster than the water.

   a. Compare the heat required to raise the temperature of 30 g of aluminum from 20°C to 40°C to the heat required to raise the temperature of 30 g of water the same amount. Which requires fewer calories? (aluminum)

   b. Use the specific heat capacities of water and aluminum to explain why the aluminum gets hot faster. (Aluminum has a smaller specific heat capacity, which means that fewer calories are required to raise the temperature per g°C)

6. Suppose that you are camping in the winter. You want to heat 30 g of water to 40°C, but all you have is 30 g of snow.

   a. The heat required to melt snow at 0°C is 80 cal/g. How much heat is required to melt 30 g of snow. (2400 cal)

   b. As the snow is melting, the temperature is not changing. How is the heat being used?

   c. You need to heat the 30 g of water you obtain from melting the snow from 0°C to 40°C. How much heat is required? (1200 cal)

   d. How much total heat is required to heat 30 g of snow to liquid water at 40°C? (3600 cal)

Making Sense:
Explain the difference between heat and temperature.

If you finish early...
You have 10 g iron at 600°C and 10 g of water at 0°C. You put the hot iron in the colder water. The specific heat capacity of water is 1 cal/g°C. The specific heat capacity of iron is 0.11 cal/g°C. For which of the two substances will the temperature change be greater? Explain your thinking.

Making Sense Discussion (10–15 min)

Major goals: The main goal of this discussion is to provide students with an opportunity to refine their understanding of heat and heat transfer. Students should come away from the lesson with the idea that heat and temperature are not the same. Heat depends on the quantity of substance, the specific heat capacity, and whether or not a phase change occurs. From an atomic view, heat is a measure of the total motion of atoms, whereas temperature is the average motion.

5. Discuss the difference between heat and temperature.

Discussion goals:
Help students to distinguish between heat and temperature. Include a discussion at the molecular level.

Sample questions:
What happened to the temperature of the water as the Cheeto burned?
Why did the temperature of the water increase?
As the temperature of the water increases, what happens to the degree of motion of the water molecules?
Why does it take more calories to increase the temperature of a larger volume of water by the same number of degrees?
What is the difference between heat and temperature?

Temperature is a measure of the average motion of the water molecules. Heat is a measure of the total motion. Explain what this means.

Points to cover:
When we transfer heat to a container of water by burning a Cheeto below the water, the temperature change of the water depends on the amount of water. A larger amount of water requires more heat transfer to raise the temperature by the same amount. Thus, heat and temperature are not the same.

Temperature is measured indirectly by measuring the expansion of a liquid as heat is transferred. By calibrating this expansion, we can create a thermometer to measure temperature. A thermometer keeps track of the average motion, or kinetic energy, of the atoms and molecules in a substance.

Heat is a measure of the total change in motion of the atoms and molecules in a substance. In other words, if you have more molecules, then more heat is needed to increase their motion. We measure heat by measuring the temperature change for a specific quantity of water. Each calorie of heat transferred raises the temperature of 1 g of water by 1°C. If you have more water, then the temperature change will be lower. The heat transferred is proportional to the mass times the temperature change.

Temperature is a measure of the average motion, or kinetic energy, of the atoms and molecules in a substance.

Heat is a measure of the total motion of all the atoms and molecules in a system. More heat is required to raise the temperature as the mass of the substances in the system is increased. The heat required is also specific to the substances, and is called the specific heat.

6. Discuss specific heat capacity of substances other than water.

Discussion goals:
Assist students in comparing the specific heat capacities of different substances.

Sample questions:
Which gets hot faster, water or metal?
Which gets cold faster, water or metal?
Which has a higher specific hear capacity, water or metal? Explain your thinking.
Suppose you want to make a "hand warmer" by heating a substance to 60°C. Should you choose a substance with a high specific heat capacity? Why or why not?

Points to cover:
Each substance has a different specific heat capacity. In other words, the number of calories required to heat 1 g sand or 1 g alcohol by 1°C is not equal to 1 calorie. Specific heat capacities for a variety of substances can be found in tables in chemistry books and on the Web.

The specific heat capacity of water is 1 cal/g°C. This is a very high specific heat capacity. It takes a lot of heat to raise the temperature of water relative to other substances. This is all too obvious if we place a metal pot with water on the stove. The pot gets hot very quickly, whereas it takes a long time for the water to boil. This is because the specific heat capacities of metals are much lower than 1 cal/g°C. For example, the specific heat capacity of aluminum is 0.22 calories/g°C. This means that it only takes 0.22 calories to raise the temperature of 1 g of aluminum by 1°C. Likewise, aluminum cools faster than water because it has less heat to transfer in order to lower its temperature.

7. Define latent heat of vaporization.

Discussion goals:
Define latent heat.

Sample questions:
Is heat required or released when ice melts?
Is heat required or released when water freezes?
Does the temperature change when ice melts?
Is heat required or released when water evaporates?
Is heat required or released when water condenses?
Does the temperature change when water boils?
From a molecular point of view, why is heat required to melt? To boil?
How does sweating keep us cool?

Points to cover:
Heat is required to change matter from solid to liquid, from solid to gas, and from liquid to gas. This is because energy is required to weaken or break the interactions between atoms and molecules. Likewise, heat is released when matter changes from gas to liquid, from gas to solid, and from liquid to solid. The heat associated with phase changes is called **latent heat.** It is expressed in calories/gram. The temperature does not change during a phase change.

Latent heat is the heat associated with a phase change and is measured in cal/g.

8. Summarize the investigation.

Construct the first part of a concept map on fire. Ask students about the evidence for fire and add their ideas. Be sure to put "Fire" in the center of a large sheet of paper so that you can add more ideas later in the unit.

Points to cover:
In this investigation we began examining the evidence for fire and determined that a fire produces heat, light (a flame), and new products (e.g., water vapor, gas, smoke, and ash). In this investigation, the heat transferred to other substances has been the major focus. To summarize, a fire is an exothermic process in which heat is transferred to substances that come in contact with the fire.

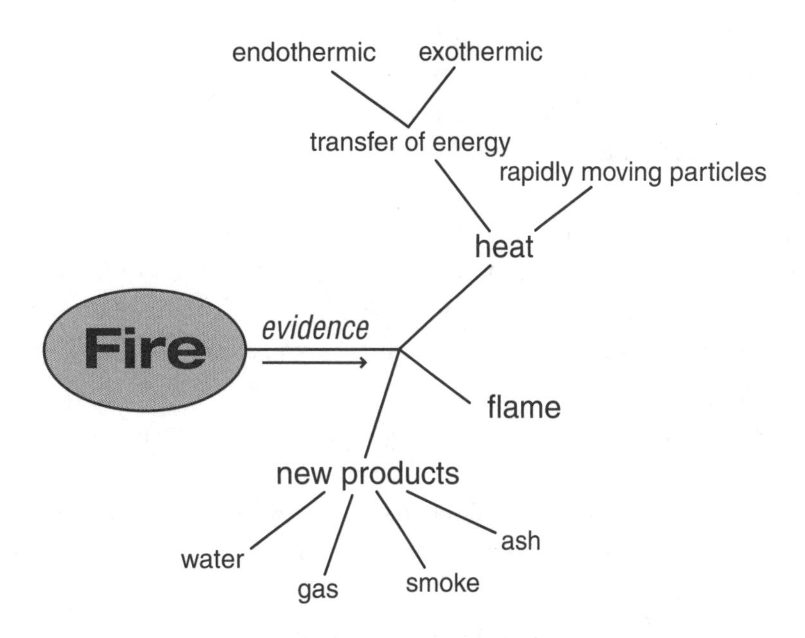

Check-in (5 min)

9. Introduce the Check-in exercise.

Write the following exercise on the board for students to complete individually.

For each pair below, explain which requires the larger amount of heat. Explain your thinking.

- Raising the temperature of 10 g of water from 20°C to 40°C or raising the temperature of 40 g of water from 20°C to 30°C.
- Raising the temperature of 20 g of water from 60°C to 80°C or from 90°C to 110°C. (Water boils at 100°C.)
- Raising the temperature of 50 g of water or 50 g of sand by 20°C. (Sand has a smaller specific heat capacity than water.)

10. Discuss the Check-in exercise.

Get a sense of the level of understanding by taking a vote, collecting students' work, or asking students to defend their choices.

Discussion goals:

Assess that students understand how the transfer of heat depends on the substance, the amount, the temperature change, and if a phase change occurs.

Sample questions:

How does the change in temperature affect the heat required?

How does the amount of substance affect the heat required?

What do you need to know to determine the calories of heat required to raise the temperature of water?

Is extra heat required to boil water? Why or why not?

Is the same amount of heat required to heat sand and water? Why or why not?

11. Wrap-up

Assist the students in summarizing what was learned in the class.

- Temperature is the measure of the average kinetic energy of a substance.
- Heat is a measure of the total kinetic energy. It depends on both mass and temperature.
- Heat and temperature are not the same. A larger quantity of water at the same temperature will transfer more heat.
- Specific heat capacity depends on the substance. More heat needs to be transferred to raise the temperature of substances with high specific heat capacities.
- Heat is transferred during a phase change, but the temperature does not change. This heat is called latent heat.

Homework

12. Assign homework.

Use the homework provided with the curriculum or assign your own.

Homework – Investigation I – Lesson 6

1. If you take a 5-minute shower, you use about 100,000 mL (25 gallons) of water. The water needs to be heated from 20°C to 40°C.
   a. How many calories do you need to warm the water for your shower?
   b. How many grams of wood do you need to burn to take a 5-minute shower? The wood releases 4000 cal/g when you heat it.
   c. How many pounds of wood do you need to burn to take a 5-minute shower? The wood releases 1,814 kcal/lb when you burn it.
2. Which mass of water requires more heat to change its temperature by the amount specified?
   a. 100 g of water from 20ºC to 60ºC.
   b. 200 g of water from 20ºC to 45ºC.
3. A piece of wood transfers 3650 calories of heat to 100 mL of water.
   a. By how much does the temperature of the water rise?
   b. If the initial temperature of the water is 20°C, what is the final temperature?
   c. If the wood weighs 4.2 g, how many calories of heat does a 1 g of wood transfer?
4. Which cup of water gets hotter?
   a. Transfer 450 calories to 100 g of water starting at 25°C.
   b. Transfer 600 calories to 200 g of water starting at 25°C.
5. Suppose you repeat the Cheeto® experiment, but you place alcohol in the soda can instead of water. The specific heat capacity of alcohol is 0.58 cal/g °C.
   a. What does it mean that alcohol has a different specific heat capacity? (a different number of calories are required to heat 1 gram of alcohol by 1 °C compared with water)
   b. How many calories are required to raise the temperature of 250 g of water by 10°C? (2500 cal)
   c. You will need fewer calories to raise the temperature of 250 g of alcohol by 10°C. Use the specific heat capacity of alcohol to explain why. (for alcohol, you only need 0.58 cal to raise the temperature of 1 g by 1°C)
   d. How many calories are required to raise the temperature of 250 g of alcohol by 10°C? (1450 cal)
   e. Suppose that you put an ice cube of the same size in the water and in the alcohol. Which has the capacity to melt more of the ice?

Burning Questions

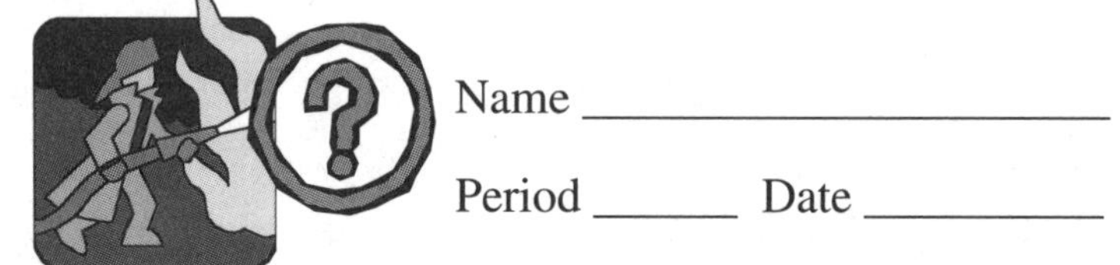

Name ____________________

Period ______ Date __________

Purpose: This activity provides you with practice solving problems involving heat and temperature.

Challenge: In this activity, you will determine the heat required to raise the temperature of the following substances to 40°C. The different substances were heated over a fire using wood as fuel.

1. Use your experience with heating things to make predictions. Rank the following substances from (1-5) with 5 requiring the most heat to raise the temperature to 40°C.

Substance	**Rank (1** least to **5** most)
30 g of water starting at 20°C	
300 g of water starting at 20°C	
30 g of water starting at 0°C	
30 g of ice starting at 0°C	
30 g aluminum pot starting at 20°C	

2. Explain your thinking.

3. Fill in the table.

CALORIES NEEDED TO RAISE THE TEMPERATURE TO 40°C							
	substance	amount	initial T	Δ T	heat needed to change phase	specific heat capacities	calories required
A	H_2O (l)	30 g	20°C	20°C	0	1 cal/g°C	600 cal
B	H_2O (l)	300 g	20°C		0	1 cal/g°C	
C	H_2O (l)	30 g	0°C	40°C	0		1200 cal
D	H_2O (s)	30 g	0°C		80 cal/g	1 cal/g°C	3600 cal
E	Al (s)	30 g	20°C		0	0.22 cal/g°C	132 cal
F	Al (s)	300 g	20°C		0	0.22 cal/g°C	

4. Your friend says, "It should take more heat to raise the temperature of 30 g of water from 0°C to 40°C compared with raising the temperature of 30 g of water or even 300 g water by 20 °C because 40ºC is a bigger change. A bigger change in temperature means more heat is needed."
   a. Your friend's conclusion is incorrect. What other factor must be considered?

b. Compare A and B. In terms of motions of water molecules, explain why it takes more wood to raise the temperature of a larger quantity of water by the same amount.

c. Compare A and C. In terms of the motions of the water molecules, explain why it takes more wood to raise the temperature of the same quantity of water by a larger amount.

5. When you boil water in an aluminum pot on the stove, the pot gets hot much faster than the water.

   a. Compare the heat required to raise the temperature of 30 g of aluminum from 20°C to 40°C to the heat required to raise the temperature of 30 g of water the same amount. Which requires fewer calories?

   b. Use the specific heat capacities of water and aluminum to explain why the aluminum gets hot faster.

6. Suppose that you are camping in the winter. You want to heat 30 g of water to 40°C, but all you have is 30 g of snow.

   a. The heat required to melt snow at 0°C is 80 cal/g. How much heat is required to melt 30 g of snow.

   b. As the snow is melting, the temperature is not changing. How is the heat being used?

   c. You need to heat the 30 g of water you obtain from melting the snow from 0°C to 40°C. How much heat is required?

   d. How much total heat is required to heat 30 g of snow to liquid water at 40°C?

Making Sense:
Explain the difference between heat and temperature.

If you finish early...
You have 10 g iron at 600°C and 10 g of water at 0°C. You put the hot iron in the colder water. The specific heat capacity of water is 1 cal/g°C. The specific heat capacity of iron is 0.11 cal/g°C. For which of the two substances will the temperature change be greater? Explain your thinking.

Unit 5: Fire

Investigation II: Conditions for Change

Contents of Investigation II *Page*

Investigation II Summary:

Conditions for Change

Lesson 1 – No Smoking Zone In this activity students are challenged to describe the conditions necessary for combustion by observing a series of demonstrations. The three sides of the fire triangle are highlighted.

Lesson 2 – You're Fired! In order to investigate what sorts of substances can be used as fuels, students examine what types of substances will combust. Students are provided with a data table and must look for patterns in the combustible and noncombustible materials. Then they are allowed to predict and test the outcome for four new substances.

Lesson 3 – All-A-Glow In the previous two lessons, we have learned that oxygen and fuels are needed for combustion. Both carbon-containing molecules and metals can serve as fuels. In this lesson, we will examine the products of combustion by writing balanced chemical equations. Students will look for patterns in the identities and amounts of reactants and products. The lesson ends with a discussion of flames, and the connection between flames and combustion reactions that occur in the gas phase.

Lesson 4 – Fuelish Choices In this lesson, students investigate the fuels involved in combustion. Their focus changes to one of examining and comparing substances in terms of their chemical formulas and energy output. They accomplish this by exploring combustion reactions in more detail. In addition students will compare calorie data to begin to make connections between energy output and chemical make-up. Finally, students will extend the Fire Chart by adding information about the fire triangle and fuels.

Lesson 5 – Sparklers In this activity students complete a laboratory procedure that results in the creation of several different sparklers, similar to those used for celebrations. The newly created sparklers must be dried in an oven for several hours. Thus the creation of the sparklers occurs on one day and the testing and processing of them on another day. After the sparklers are created and placed in an appropriate container for drying by the instructor, students must finish a worksheet. The focus of this lesson is two-pronged. First it allows students to explore the combustion of metals. Second, this lesson sets up an introduction to the concept of a fourth condition necessary for fire – a chemical chain reaction.

Lesson 6 – Burning Questions There are two main, but overlapping, concepts introduced during this lesson: the fire tetrahedron and the chemistry of explosions. Students begin this lesson by burning and observing the sparklers they created in the previous lesson. The sparklers lead into the introduction of a fourth condition necessary for fire – a sustained chemical chain reaction. Students will observe several demonstrations by the instructor that show how surface area can influence the rate of a reaction and result in explosions.

BEFORE CLASS…

LESSON 1 – No Smoking Zone

Key Ideas:
The conditions that are necessary for fire are often summarized in the fire triangle. Oxygen, fuel, and a spark constitute the three sides of the fire triangle. Later we will see that a fourth condition is also necessary for fire to occur. By limiting or removing one of these necessary elements, a fire can be controlled or extinguished.

What Takes Place:
This lesson consists of several demonstrations. Students view the demonstrations with an eye toward determining the conditions necessary for fire. The first demonstration involves a homemade cigarette smoking machine that collects the products of tobacco combustion (or combustion of a roll of paper), as well as demonstrates the three sides of the fire triangle. Second, dry paper and paper dipped in isopropanol are burned. If water is present, the paper does not burn. The lesson ends with a discussion of ways to put out a fire.

TEACHER ALERT:
In order to complete this activity a cigarette will be lit and "smoked" by an apparatus in class. Thus, you should make sure that students are not asthmatic or allergic to cigarette smoke prior to the demonstration. Open several windows, if possible. NOTE: You can also use paper and/or tissue paper rolled to the size of a cigarette. Hopefully, the opportunity to talk about the dangers of smoking will outweigh the presence of a small amount of smoke in the room.

Set up "smoking machine"
Construct your "smoking machine" before class. Use a plastic soda bottle with a cap. Carefully cut a hole in the bottle cap the size of the tubing and insert the tubing through the hole. Use clay around the base of the tubing to completely seal the hole in the cap. Place about ten cotton balls inside the bottle. Keep at least one fresh cotton ball for comparison. You should practice using the machine before class.

Set up CO_2 balloon
Before class, prepare a CO_2 balloon by filling it up with your breath and tying it off.

Materials: (for one class)
- Student worksheet
- 1–2 unfiltered cigarettes (optional: rolled paper may be substituted)
- 1 plastic 2-L cola bottle with cap
- 1 piece of 6-inch plastic tubing
- clay to seal hole in cap

- tape
- 1 package non-filter cigarettes (1–2 cigarettes per class)
- 10 cotton balls
- 1 500-mL beaker with ~50 mL water (labeled water)
- 1 500-mL beaker with ~50 mL isopropanol (rubbing alcohol) (labeled isopropanol)
- 1 500-mL beaker with ~25 mL water mixed with ~25 mL isopropanol (labeled 50/50 water/isopropanol)
- 1 pair tongs
- 1 clay flower pot with sand (for putting out paper fire)
- 3 paper strips (3 long strips from a single piece of paper, ~ 3" x 11")
- 1 dollar bill (optional, for effect: a strip of paper can be substituted)
- 1 balloon, blow up and label CO_2
- 1 ring stand with a ring
- 1 dowel with taper candle attached
- matches

Investigation II – Conditions for Change

LESSON 1 – No Smoking Zone

In this activity students are challenged to describe the conditions necessary for combustion by observing a series of demonstrations. The three sides of the fire triangle – oxygen, fuel, and a spark – are highlighted. Students have an opportunity to "see" the products of the combustion of tobacco and its additives, and to consider the dangers of inhaling these products. In the Making Sense Discussion, combustion is defined and by examining the conditions necessary for fire, students are able to explore how to extinguish a fire.

Exploring the Topic (5–10 min)

1. Introduce the ChemCatalyst exercise.

Write the following exercise on the board for students to complete individually.

- What conditions are necessary for a fire to take place? Describe at least two situations that result in fire.

2. Discuss the ChemCatalyst exercise.

Use the discussion to get a sense of students' initial ideas.

Discussion goals:
Use the students' responses as a jumping off place for a discussion of the conditions for fire.

Sample questions:
Describe an example of conditions that result in fire.
Do all substances burn?
What conditions allow you to put out a fire?
Is a cigarette an example of burning? Of fire? Explain your answer.

3. Explain the purpose of today's activity.

If you wish you can write the main question on the board.

Points to cover:
Tell students they will be gathering information to answer the question: "What conditions are necessary for fire?"

Activity – No Smoking Zone (15 min)

4. Introduce the activity. (Worksheet)

Pass out the worksheet and explain the activity. Give students a chance to fill out the table in the worksheet as you do the demonstrations.

Most of these demonstrations are easy to set up. You can choose to do all or only some of them.

SAFETY NOTE: Wear safety glasses while performing these demonstrations. Keep hair and loose clothing away from flames. Make sure students are at least 10 feet away from the demonstration table. Be sure to have a fire extinguisher available.

Demonstrations:

DEMO 1 – "Smoking Machine"

Materials:
1 cigarette (or a piece of paper rolled to the size of a cigarette)
1 plastic 2-L cola bottle with cap
1 piece of 6-inch plastic tubing
clay to seal hole in cap
tape

10 cotton balls
lighter or matches

Squeeze the plastic bottle to force the air out. Place an unlit cigarette (or roll of paper) firmly in the end of the tubing. Light the cigarette with a match or lighter. Loosen the cap a little bit and begin pumping the bottle slowly and steadily. When the cigarette is finished, put it out. Examine the cotton balls for evidence of the products of burning tobacco. (If you use the machine to smoke several cigarettes before class you can increase the amount of tar on the cotton balls to make the evidence more dramatic.)

DEMO 2 – Paper

Materials:
1 500-mL beaker with ~50 mL water (labeled "water")
1 500-mL beaker with ~50 mL isopropanol (rubbing alcohol) (labeled "isopropanol")
1 500-mL beaker ~25 mL water mixed with ~25 mL isopropanol
(labeled "50/50 water/isopropanol")
1 pair tongs
1 clay flower pot with sand (for putting out paper fire)
3 paper strips (3 long strips from a single piece of paper, ~ 3" x 11")
1 dollar bill
1 lit candle
matches

Light a candle to use for the next set of demos.

Burn Paper. Hold a strip of paper (~3" x 11") with tongs. Ignite the paper with the flame from the candle, and let the paper burn. Hold the paper over the clay flowerpot. Extinguish the flame in the sand in the flowerpot after students have observed.

Wet paper. Hold a second strip of paper (~3" x 11") with tongs. Dip the paper in water. Try to ignite the paper with the flame from the candle.

Drunk paper. Hold a third strip of paper (~3 x 11") with tongs. Dip the paper in isopropanol. Allow some of the isopropanol to evaporate so that it is not dripping from the paper. Carefully, ignite the paper with the flame from the candle, and let the paper burn. Hold the paper over the clay flowerpot. Extinguish the flame in the sand in the flowerpot after students have observed.

Dollar bill (You can ask for a student to donate a dollar bill ☺. Paper can be used instead.) Hold a dollar bill with tongs. Dip the dollar bill in the 50:50 mixture of isopropanol and water. When you dip the bill in the mixture, keep the tong clamp in place, but let go just enough to make sure that the bill gets wet where the tongs are holding it. If a spot is left dry, it could ignite later. Bring a corner of the dollar bill close to the candle to ignite the isopropanol. The dollar bill will become engulfed in flames until the isopropanol is gone. As you ignite the bill, be ready to drop the bill in the water in case the bill does burn a little near the top.

DEMO 3 – Balloon

Materials:
1 balloon, blow up and label CO_2
1 ring stand with a ring
1 dowel with taper candle attached
1 lit candle
matches

Carbon dioxide balloon. Prepare and label the balloon before class. Set the CO_2 balloon on the ring of the ring stand. Light the taper candle on the dowel. Hold under the balloon until it pops.

Worksheet

Instructions: You will observe several demonstrations. Predict what you will observe. After each demonstration, record your observations.

Demonstration	**Prediction** What will you observe when lit?	**Observation**
Smoking machine	**answers will vary**	**Cigarette burns with a glow, there is smoke, and it gets smaller**

Paper		**Paper burns with a yellow flame**
Wet paper (paper + water)		**Paper does not burn**
Drunk paper (paper + isopropanol)		**Paper burns with a blue flame**
Dollar bill (dollar+water+isopropanol)		**Dollar bill is engulfed with flames, but does not burn**
Carbon dioxide balloon		**Balloon pops**

Answer the following questions:

1. Which demonstrations surprised you and did not match your predictions?
2. What was needed to test each of these substances to see if they burn? (a light or match or spark)
3. Substances that burn are fuels. List the four fuels used in the demonstrations. (cigarette, paper, isopropanol, hydrogen)
4. Substances that do not burn are non-flammable. List two substances from the demonstration that are non-flammable. (water and carbon dioxide)
5. Why do you think the dollar bill did not burn? (The heat from the burning of the isopropanol was transferred to the water, rather than to the paper.)
6. Many fire extinguishers are filled with a gas. Which gas would you use in a fire extinguisher? Explain your reasoning.

Smoking machine

1. Why did the instructor have to squeeze the bottle repeatedly while the cigarette was burning?
2. What conditions are necessary to get the cigarette to burn?
3. What is the fuel in this demonstration?
4. If there is no flame on the cigarette is it still burning? Would you consider a cigarette to be an example of a fire? Why or why not?
5. What evidence do you have that burning a cigarette is a chemical reaction?
6. What evidence do you have from this demonstration that smoking a cigarette may be harmful?

Making sense:
Pick three things from the list below to build a fire. Explain your choices.

water	aluminum	helium	sugar
oxygen	wax	match	coal

If you finish early...
Why isn't there a flame when a cigarette burns?

Making Sense Discussion (10–15 min)

Major goals: Students should be able to articulate the conditions generally required for a fire and relate those conditions to the combustion of a cigarette and other fuels. Teachers can take this opportunity to discuss the hazards of inhaling combustion products from tobacco and tobacco additives. Students should consider how the conditions could be manipulated to put out a fire.

5. Discuss the conditions necessary for a fire.

Discussion goals:
Assist students in articulating the conditions necessary for a fire.

Sample questions:
What conditions are necessary for a fire to take place?
What is the fire triangle? Where did you learn about it?
Which things accounted for the three sides of the fire triangle in the demonstrations?
What evidence do you have that oxygen alone is not sufficient for a fire?
Why do you think the wet paper and the dollar bill did not burn?

FUEL
OXYGEN
combustion
HEAT

Points to cover:
The three sides of the fire triangle were evident in today's lesson. The cigarette, the paper, and the balloons were lit with a match – this represents the spark that is necessary. The squeezing of the bottle provided sufficient oxygen for burning the cigarette. And the tobacco (with its many ingredients), the paper, and the hydrogen served as fuel.

Oxygen alone is not sufficient for a fire. You need a spark and fuel. Oxygen isn't a fuel.

The dollar bill did not burn because it was wet (with water). The match lit the alcohol. The heat transferred from the burning alcohol evaporated some of the water. Since water boils at 100°C, as long as water is present, the temperature does not get high enough to ignite the paper. This is why damp fuel does not burn easily. In contrast, isopropanol is a fuel. The paper dipped in isopropanol with no water does burn.

6. Define the term combustion.

Discussion goals:

Introduce the term combustion. Discuss the relationship between fire and combustion.

Sample questions:

What do you think the term combustion means?
How is combustion the same or different than a fire?
Can something combust without being on fire?
Is a cigarette an example of burning? Of fire? Of combustion? Explain your answer.

Points to cover:
A chemical reaction that results in fire is also called a **combustion reaction.** Combustion is generally defined as a process by which a substance undergoes a reaction that results in the release of heat and light. Combustion is often referred to as burning. Every reaction that results in fire is considered a combustion reaction, however, not every combustion reaction results in the production of a fire.

As we observed in today's activity, it is possible for a substance to burn without producing a flame. Cigarettes glow and they release a great deal of heat. A cigarette is an example of a combustion reaction that does not result in what we usually think of when we imagine a fire.

Combustion reaction: The reaction of a fuel with oxygen, resulting in the production of heat and light.

7. Discuss how a fire can be extinguished.

Discussion goals:
Assist students in articulating how a fire can be extinguished.

Sample questions:

What would happen to the cigarette if the bottle were not squeezed regularly?
Would a wet cigarette burn? Why not?
How can you put out a cigarette?
How does a CO_2 fire extinguisher work?
What causes some fires to be really smoky? What is this evidence of?

Points to cover:
Combustion reactions that result in fire are typically extinguished by limiting the supply of oxygen reaching the fuel. This can be achieved by covering the fire (e.g., with a blanket or sand) so that oxygen from the air cannot reach the fuel to react. Another way is to blow the oxygen away with a large amount of carbon

dioxide gas (e.g., from a fire extinguisher). This essentially "smothers" the fire, by not allowing oxygen near it. A CO_2 extinguisher is like a "gas blanket."

Pouring water on a fire also works to extinguish the fire. The heat from the fire is used to evaporate the water. Since water boils at 100°C, this rapidly reduces the temperature such that there is not enough heat to continue the burning of the fuel. This is why it is not possible to burn damp fuel. The heat from the match warms the water instead of igniting the combustion reaction.

When a fire is smoky, it usually means it is not burning that well. The fuel may be damp or not getting enough oxygen to burn well. The presence of smoke is evidence of incomplete combustion - this means the fuel is not completely burned and broken down. Smoke consists of bits of fuel and combustion products mixed with gases.

8. Discuss combustion as it relates to cigarette ingredients. (optional)

Points to cover:
The cotton balls collect some of the by-products of a burning cigarette. You can use this as a segue to talk about the effects of smoking on our lungs and our bodies. There is a list of 600 additives that are approved by the United States Government for use in the manufacture of cigarettes. Phillip Morris lists 115 ingredients in its tobacco alone and hundreds of others in its cigarette papers and filters. Most of these ingredients are included in the tobacco in order to enhance or influence the "flavor" of the cigarette. These ingredient lists are too long to include here, but are available on the Phillip Morris website:

http://www.philipmorrisusa.com/en/product_facts/ingredients/tobacco_ingredients.asp

Below are just a few of the items mentioned on the website that are present in cigarettes (you may recognize some of them from the *Smells* unit!). Remember, most of these substances are approved for use in food items, *without* being burned and turned into combustion products. Thus, this list only contains the *reactants* that will be burned. However, over 4000 chemical *products* are produced when a cigarette is burned, many of them cancer causing.

Acetic acid	Peppermint oil
Ammonia	Propylene glycol
Benzaldehyde	Sugar – sucrose
Butyric acid	Celery seed oil
Citronella oil	Isoamyl hexanoate
Geraniol	Geranium rose oil
Glycerol	Vanillin

Ammonium magnesium phosphate (papers)
Calcium carbonate (papers)
Polyvinyl alcohol (adhesive)

Obviously, these ingredients are approved as reactants, but the resultant products of the burning have not necessarily been approved. Some of the products of burning tobacco are hydrogen cyanide, carbon monoxide, formaldehyde, and nitrogen dioxide. Carbon monoxide is a toxin, which limits your body's ability to transport oxygen to the cells. That is why cigarette smokers often feel tired. Hydrogen cyanide has been used as a chemical weapon during wartime. Formaldehyde is considered moderately toxic, and is a probable carcinogen.

Check-in (5 min)

9. Introduce the Check-in exercise.

Write the following exercise on the board for students to complete individually.

- There is a small fire in the trashcan in your classroom. Name three things your teacher can do to put out the fire. Explain how each method works.

10. Discuss the Check-in exercise.

Get a sense of the level of understanding by taking a vote, collecting students' work, or asking students to defend their choices.

Discussion goals:

Make sure students understand the conditions necessary for combustion reactions.

Sample questions:

What conditions are necessary for fire?
How can you alter the conditions to put out the fire?
Why is it less likely that there will be a forest fire just after it rains?

11. Wrap-up

Assist the students in summarizing what was learned in the class.

- Combustion is defined as a reaction of a fuel with oxygen, which releases heat and light.
- Dry fuel, a spark of some sort, and oxygen are the three items necessary for combustion.
- Limiting the supply of oxygen, or adding water, extinguishes fires.
- Cigarette smoking is a form of combustion that has many by-products, several of them harmful to your health.

Homework

12. Assign homework.

Use the homework provided with the curriculum or assign your own.

Homework – Investigation II – Lesson 1

1. What evidence is there from this demonstration that smoking may not be a safe activity?

2. Name at least three different ways that you can put out a fire. Explain why each method works.

3. Which of the following methods can be used to put out a cigarette? Explain why each does or does not work.

   a. Push the burning end of the cigarette against an ashtray.

   b. Put water on the cigarette.

   c. Blow oxygen gas on the cigarette.

   d. Blow carbon dioxide gas on a cigarette.

No Smoking Zone

Name: ____________________

Period: ____ Date: ___________

Purpose: By observing a series of demonstrations you will explore the conditions that lead to fire.

Instructions: You will observe several demonstrations. Predict what you will observe. After each demonstration, record your observations.

Demonstration	Prediction What will you observe when lit?	Observation
Smoking machine		
Paper		
Wet paper (paper + water)		
Drunk paper (paper + isopropanol)		
Dollar bill (dollar+water+isopropanol)		
Carbon dioxide balloon		

Answer the following questions:

1. Which demonstrations surprised you and did not match your predictions?

2. What was needed to test each of these substances to see if they burn?

3. Substances that burn are fuels. List the four fuels used in the demonstrations.

4. Substances that do not burn are non-flammable. List two substances from the demonstration that are non-flammable.

5. Why do you think the dollar bill did not burn?

6. Many fire extinguishers are filled with a gas. Which gas would you use in a fire extinguisher? Explain your reasoning.

Smoking machine

1. Why did the instructor have to squeeze the bottle repeatedly while the cigarette was burning?

2. What conditions are necessary to get the cigarette to burn?

3. What is the fuel in this demonstration?

4. If there is no flame on the cigarette is it still burning? Would you consider a cigarette to be an example of a fire? Why or why not?

5. What evidence do you have that burning a cigarette is a chemical reaction?

6. What evidence do you have <u>from this demonstration</u>, that smoking a cigarette is harmful?

Making sense:

Pick three things from the list below to build a fire. Explain your choices.

water	aluminum	helium	sugar
oxygen	wax	match	coal

If you finish early...

Why isn't there a flame when a cigarette burns?

BEFORE CLASS…

LESSON 2 – You're Fired!

Key Ideas:
The term combustion is synonymous with what we informally call "burning." Not all substances combust (or burn) in oxygen to release heat and light. Most ionic substances do not combust. Most molecular covalent compounds containing carbon are combustible. Metals also react with oxygen, and are considered combustible under the right conditions.

What Takes Place:
Students are provided with data on whether or not a number of different substances will combust. They will examine the data looking for patterns. Then they will predict whether or not four new substances will combust, based on their conclusions. Finally, these four new substances will be available in the classroom so the instructor may attempt to burn them and students may test their predictions.

Set up: Before class, set up an alcohol burner with oil. Gather the other materials so that you are prepared to complete the demonstrations in Part II of the activity.

Materials: (For each class)
- Student worksheet
- 1 piece of steel wool (fine mesh)
- 50 mL of vinegar in a beaker
- thermometer
- 1 bunsen burner (or a candle)
- 50 mL lamp oil
- 1 alcohol burner
- 1 teaspoon salt
- 1 watch glass
- 1 piece of chalk
- 12" piece of aluminum foil
- 50 mL vinegar
- 2 oven mitts (can be found in *Weather* kit)
- 1 candle
- matches

Investigation II – Conditions for Change

LESSON 2 – You're Fired!

In order to investigate what sorts of substances can be used as fuels, students examine what types of substances will combust. Students are provided with a data table and must look for patterns in the combustible and noncombustible materials. Then they are allowed to predict and test the outcome for four new substances.

Exploring the Topic (5–10 min)

1. Introduce the ChemCatalyst exercise.

Write the following exercise on the board for students to complete individually.

- Name three substances that will combust or burn.
- Name three substances that do not combust.

2. Discuss the ChemCatalyst exercise.

Use the discussion to get a sense of students' initial ideas. Make a list of substances that students say burn and don't burn during the discussion.

Discussion goals:
Use the students' written responses to stimulate an open-ended discussion of what substances will combust.

Sample questions:
What are some substances that will combust?
What are some substances that do not combust?
What do you think is similar about the substances that combust?
What is similar about the substances that don't combust?
Are wet things combustible?
Do liquids combust?
Do all solids combust?
Is tarnishing a form of combustion?
Do metals combust?
What differences do you notice in the list of substances that burn and don't burn?

It is likely that students will think that metals do not combust. Ask them about tarnishing. Do the steel wool demonstration described below to help students decide whether tarnishing is a form of combustion.

3. Expand on the language of fire.

Points to cover:
So far we have provided some loose definitions of the terms **burn, fire,** and **combustion.** One of the goals of the *Fire* unit is to refine students' definitions and understanding of these terms. For now, we will use the working definition that burning and combustion are the same process. When we ask if something combusts, we are essentially asking if it burns. Remember, combustion is one category of chemical reaction. It is a reaction with oxygen that releases heat and light. A fire is one type of combustion reaction. Usually, when we call something a fire, it is because a flame is present. Whereas a fire is associated with a flame, some combustion reactions only produce a glow (and no flame).

4. Discuss the combustion of metals.

Do the following demonstration to help student decide whether metals combust.

Demonstration – Combustion of aluminum

Materials
12" piece of aluminum foil
50 mL of vinegar in a beaker
1 thermometer
2 oven mitts

Dip the aluminum foil in the vinegar for about a minute. Do not dry it. Using oven mitts, wrap the foil around the thermometer. Observe the temperature. (The temperature will rise a small amount due to combustion of the aluminum. We use oven mitts to show the temperature increase is not from our hands.)

Sample questions:
Why do you think that the temperature rises?
How might tarnishing of metals be related to combustion?
Provide evidence that metals undergo slow combustion.

Points to cover:
In describing things that combust, students may say that metals do not. Acknowledge that in our experience, metals normally do not combust; in fact, we count on this property of machined metals: we use metal implements for tending a fire, and we cook in metal pans! However, metals *do* combust (and some ignite even just coming in contact with air or water, e.g., sodium, magnesium, aluminum). However, there are certain conditions that normally prevent the metals we use from combusting: metals are usually coated in oil, or in the case of aluminum, a thin coating of oxide; and metals are dense, and therefore the atoms in the interior are protected. In the absence of these protections, metals can combust (and they certainly tarnish, which is a slower process of combustion). In this demonstration, the temperature rise is an indication that the aluminum is reacting.

5. Explain the purpose of today's activity.

If you wish you can write the main question on the board.

Points to cover:
Tell students that in today's activity they will test and examine data about substances that combust. They will then predict the outcome for several new substances. The question for today is, "How can we predict what will combust?"

Activity – You're Fired! (15 min)

6. Introduce the activity. (Worksheet)

Pass out the worksheet. Explain to students that this activity has two parts. In Part I they will be examining some data and looking for patterns to determine what combusts. In Part II students will be making predictions for four new substances. They will be able to observe as you test the combustibility of the four substances through demonstration.

Part I: What Combusts?

Complete the table, filling in the appropriate type of bonding. Then examine the table and look for patterns.

Data Table:

Substance	Chemical Formula	Type of Bond	Combust?
Water	H_2O	molecular covalent	no
Wood	chains of $C_6H_{12}O_6$ units	extended covalent	yes
Baking soda	$NaHCO_3$	ionic	no
Ethanol	CH_3CH_2OH	**molecular covalent**	yes
Zinc oxide	ZnO	**ionic**	no
Copper	Cu	metal	yes
Hexane	$CH_3CH_2CH_2CH_2CH_2CH_3$	**molecular covalent**	yes
Magnesium	Mg	**metal**	yes
Carbon dioxide	CO_2	**molecular covalent**	no
Hydrogen	H_2	**molecular covalent**	yes
Helium	He	**atomic**	no

1. Make a list of patterns that you discover in the substances that combust.
2. Make a list of patterns that you discover in the substances that do not combust.
3. Do you expect octane (C_8H_{18}) to combust? Why or why not?
4. Do you expect calcium chloride ($CaCl_2$) to combust? Why or why not?
5. Do you expect metals to combust? Why or why not?

Part II: Make Predictions and Test Them

Materials for the demonstration for Part II:
50 mL lamp oil
1 alcohol burner
1 teaspoon salt
1 watch glass
1 piece of chalk
1 piece of steel wool
50 mL vinegar (optional: to clean the steel wool)
1 candle
matches

Demonstration:
Try to burn the substances in the data table in Part II. Put the oil in an alcohol burner and light it. Put the sodium chloride (NaCl) on a watch glass and attempt to set it on fire with a match or candle (it won't burn). Hold a piece of chalk ($CaCO_3$) in a candle flame (it won't burn). Dip the steel wool (Fe) in vinegar and then into a flame. The steel wool will glow brightly.

SAFETY NOTE: Make sure you are wearing goggles, have your hair tied back, and are not wearing any loose clothing, especially loose sleeves.

Part II: Worksheet questions:

6. Examine the four substances in the table below. Predict whether or not they will combust based on the patterns you discovered earlier.

Substance	Chemical Formula	Combust? (prediction)	Combust? (outcome)
Lamp oil	$C_{21}H_{39}O_6$ (one example)		**yes**
Sodium chloride	NaCl		**no**
Calcium carbonate	$CaCO_3$		**no**
Iron	Fe		**yes**

7. What did you base your predictions on?

8. Record your observations as your teacher attempts to burn the four substances in the table. If any of your predictions was wrong, reflect and explain how you might think about your predictions differently.

Making sense:
Based on your data, what generalizations can you make about substances that combust?
What generalizations can you make about substances that ***do not*** combust?

If you finish early...
Does oxygen combust? Explain why or why not.

Making Sense Discussion (10–15 min)

Major goals: The main purpose of this discussion is for students to begin to identify patterns in combustion. Students should come away with some generalizations regarding combustible materials and their chemical make-up, and should be able to make some predictions. The main goal is for students to continue to build a foundation of understanding about *why* things combust by being introduced to what substances combust.

7. Summarize and clarify patterns of combustion.

You may wish to divide all of the substances in the data tables into two categories on the board (Combust and Do Not Combust), so that students can see the chemical formulas grouped together, and make more sense of them.

Discussion goals:
Help students to understand the chemical nature of substances that combust.

Sample questions:
What did you base your predictions on in Part II of the activity?
How does combustion appear to be related to bonding?
According to today's class, what types of substances would make good fuels?
Why do you think some substances with oxygen combust, while others don't burn at all? (Some compounds have already reacted with all the oxygen they can.)

Combust	Do Not Combust
$CH_3CH_2CH_2OH$	
$C_6H_{12}O_6$ units (wood)	H_2O
CH_3CH_2OH	CO_2
$CH_3CH_2CH_2CH_2CH_2CH_3$	ZnO
$C_{21}H_{39}O_6$ (one example)	$NaHCO_3$
H_2	NaCl
Cu	$CaCO_3$
Fe	
Mg	

Points to cover:

This activity allows us to come up with some broad generalizations regarding combustion of substances. In general

- **Most ionic compounds are not combustible.**
- **Most molecular covalent compounds are combustible (especially those that contain carbon and hydrogen). These compounds make good fuels.**
- **Most metallic compounds are combustible** – however, most do not produce a flame.
- **Substances that contain a high percentage of oxygen atoms may not be combustible because they may not be able to react with any more oxygen.**
- **Water and carbon dioxide do not combust.** In fact, they are used as fire extinguishers because they do not burn.

From the evidence in today's class we would conclude that ionic substances are not combustible. This is true. Ionic salts rarely combine with oxygen in a combustion reaction. Ionic compounds do not make good fuels.

Also, for the most part molecular covalent compounds combust. The general rule is that those molecular covalent substances that contain mainly carbon and hydrogen combust. However, water and carbon dioxide are molecular covalent molecules and they don't combust.

Finally, metals appear to combust. While the reaction of metals will produce heat, sometimes the light that is released is not detectable to the human eye. At other times the light that is released is almost blinding, as is the case when magnesium metal reacts with oxygen. However, the combustion of most metals does not produce a flame. Remember, not everything that combusts results in what we call a fire. We'll explore why this is, later in the unit.

Check-in (5 min)

8. Introduce the Check-in exercise.

Write the following exercise on the board for students to complete individually.

- Which of the following substances are likely to combust? What is your reasoning?

  CH_4, methane $CaBr_2$, calcium bromide Na, sodium

9. Discuss the Check-in exercise.

Get a sense of the level of understanding by taking a vote, collecting students' work, or asking students to defend their choices.

Discussion goals:

Make sure students know how to apply the generalizations they came up with regarding combustion.

Students should predict that methane and sodium will combust, while calcium bromide would not combust. The methane is a carbon and hydrogen based covalent compound. Sodium is a metal. The calcium bromide is ionic.

10. Wrap-up

Assist the students in summarizing what was learned in the class.

- Most ionic salts do not combust.
- Most molecular covalent compounds do combust.
- Most metals combust. Most metals do not produce a flame when they combust. Most metals combust very slowly.
- Substances that already contain a high percentage of oxygen atoms are less apt to be combustible.
- Carbon dioxide and water do not combust. They are the products of combustion.

Homework

11. Assign homework.

Use the homework provided with the curriculum or assign your own.

Homework – Investigation II – Lesson 2

1. Predict whether or not the following substances will combust. Provide some sort of evidence for each one of your answers.

   a. S, sulfur
   b. CH_4, methane
   c. Al_2O_3, aluminum oxide
   d. HCOOH, formic acid
   e. $BaCl_2$, barium chloride
   f. MgO, magnesium oxide
   g. C_6H_6, benzene
   h. He, helium

2. Write the combustion equations for the following substances:

   a. S, sulfur
   b. CH_4, methane
   c. H_2, hydrogen
   d. C_6H_6, benzene
   e. Ca, calcium
   f. CH_3OH, methanol

You're Fired!

Name: ______________________

Period: ____ Date: ____________

Student Worksheet

Purpose: The goal of this lesson is to allow you to make generalizations about substances that combust and substances that do not combust.

Part I: What Combusts?

Fill the appropriate bonding in the table below. Use the data table to assist you in answering the questions below.

Data Table:

Substance	Chemical Formula	Type of Bond	Combust?
Water	H_2O	molecular covalent	no
Wood	chains of $C_6H_{12}O_6$ units	extended covalent	yes
Baking soda	$NaHCO_3$	ionic	no
Ethanol	CH_3CH_2OH		yes
Zinc oxide	ZnO		no
Copper	Cu	metal	yes
Hexane	$CH_3CH_2CH_2CH_2CH_2CH_3$		yes
Magnesium	Mg		yes
Carbon dioxide	CO_2		no
Hydrogen	H_2		yes
Helium	He		no

1. Make a list of patterns that you discover in the substances that combust.

2. Make a list of patterns that you discover in the substances that do not combust.

3. Do you expect octane (C_8H_{18}) to combust? Why or why not?

4. Do you expect calcium chloride ($CaCl_2$) to combust? Why or why not?

5. Do you expect metals to combust? Why or why not?

Part II: Make Predictions and Test Them

6. Examine the four substances in the table below. Predict whether or not they will combust based on the patterns you discovered earlier.

Substance	**Chemical Formula**	**Combust? (prediction)**	**Combust? (outcome)**
Oil	$C_{21}H_{39}O_6$ (one example)		
Sodium chloride	$NaCl$		
Calcium carbonate	$CaCO_3$		
Iron	Fe		

7. What did you base your predictions on?

8. Record your observations as your teacher attempts to burn the four substances in the table. If any of your predictions was wrong, reflect and explain how you might think about your predictions differently.

Making sense:

Based on your data, what generalizations can you make about substances that combust?

What generalizations can you make about substances that ***do not*** combust?

If you finish early...

Does oxygen combust? Explain why or why not.

LESSON 3 – All-A-Glow

Key Ideas:
When carbon compounds are burned they produce carbon dioxide, water, and heat as products. Flames are the result of heated gases that are produced during a combustion reaction. These heated gases emit light. Combustion reactions that don't produce gases don't have flames. When metals combust, metal oxides and heat are produced. The metals and metal oxides are solids. A glow is observed on the solid as the combustion reaction proceeds, but there is no flame.

What Takes Place:
Students examine balanced chemical equations for a number of combustion reactions. They examine the combustion of carbon-containing molecules to look for patterns that depend on the composition of the fuel. Students also examine reactions of metals and metal salts with oxygen. The lesson ends with a discussion as to why a flame is observed for the combustion of carbon-containing molecules, whereas only a glow is observed for the combustion of metals.

Materials: (For each class)
- Student worksheet

Investigation II – Conditions for Change

LESSON 3 – All-A-Glow

In the previous two lessons, we learned that oxygen and fuels are needed for combustion. Both carbon-containing molecules and metals can serve as fuels. In this lesson, we will examine the products of combustion by writing balanced chemical equations. Students will look for patterns in the identities and amounts of reactants and products. The lesson ends with a discussion of flames, and the connection between flames and combustion reactions that occur in the gas phase.

Exploring the Topic (5–10 min)

1. Introduce the ChemCatalyst exercise.

Write the following exercise on the board for students to complete individually.

The following table shows the balanced chemical equations for four combustion reactions.

Substance	Combustion reaction
methane	$CH_4 + 2\,O_2 \rightarrow CO_2 + 2\,H_2O$
ethanol	$C_2H_6O + 3\,O_2 \rightarrow 2\,CO_2 + 3\,H_2O$
glucose	$C_6H_{12}O_6 + 6\,O_2 \rightarrow 6\,CO_2 + 6\,H_2O$
magnesium	$2\,Mg + O_2 \rightarrow 2\,MgO$

- List three patterns you notice.

2. Discuss the ChemCatalyst exercise.

Use the discussion to get a sense of students' initial ideas.

Discussion goals:

Use the students' written responses to stimulate an open-ended discussion of chemical equations for combustion reactions.

Sample questions:

Are the reactions balanced?
Which substances in the combustion reactions are fuels?
What are the products of combustion?
What similarities do you notice for the combustion of the three carbon-containing molecules?
How is the combustion of magnesium different from the other three?
What do all four combustion reactions have in common?

3. Explore the balancing of combustion equations.

Write the skeleton equation below on the board for the combustion of ethane. Ask students to assist you with balancing equations.

$$C_2H_6 + O_2 \rightarrow CO_2 + H_2O$$

Discussion goals:

Assist students in understanding the pros and cons of different stoichiometric representations.

Sample questions:

Balance the equation on the board for the combustion of ethane.

$$2\,C_2H_6 + 7\,O_2 \rightarrow 4\,CO_2 + 6\,H_2O$$

What if we were interested in looking at only one mole of the fuel at a time, how would we change the equation? (Divide coefficients by 2)

$$C_2H_6 + 3.5\,O_2 \rightarrow 2\,CO_2 + 3\,H_2O$$

What is the ratio of ethane molecules to oxygen molecules that react? (2:7)

How many molecules of water can you make by combusting one molecule of ethane? Which equation did you use to answer the question?

What advantages are there to the two different representations?

Points to cover:

The first balanced equation allows us to look at all the compounds in terms of whole numbers. Thus, two molecules of ethane react with seven molecules of oxygen to produce four carbon dioxide molecules and six water molecules. The second balanced equation allows us to consider every compound in terms of one unit of ethane (whether it be one molecule or one mole). Often it is more useful to consider a stoichiometric equation in terms of one particular species – in this case, we are focusing on the fuel being combusted.

4. Explain the purpose of today's activity.

If you wish you can write the main question on the board.

Points to cover:

Tell students they will be examining chemical equations for a number of combustion reactions. They will examine patterns in the identities and amounts of reactants and products. The question for today is: "How can we write a chemical equation to describe a combustion reaction?"

Activity – All-A-Glow (15 min)

5. Introduce the activity. (Worksheet)

Pass out the worksheet. Ask students to work individually.

Answer the following questions:

1. Molecules containing carbon and hydrogen are called alkanes. Alkanes react with oxygen to produce carbon dioxide, water, and a fire.

   a. Draw the structural formulas for ethane (C_2H_6), and butane (C_4H_{10}).

   b. The reactions for methane, ethane, and hexane are balanced in the table. Balance the reactions for propane, butane, and pentane. (Solve for one unit of fuel in each case.)

Combustion Reactions of Alkanes							
methane	CH_4	+	$2\ O_2$	→	CO_2	+	$2\ H_2O$
ethane	C_2H_6	+	$3.5\ O_2$	→	$2\ CO_2$	+	$3\ H_2O$
propane	C_3H_8	+	**5** O_2	→	**3** CO_2	+	**4** H_2O
butane	C_4H_{10}	+	**6.5** O_2	→	**4** CO_2	+	**5** H_2O
pentane	C_5H_{12}	+	**8** O_2	→	**5** CO_2	+	**6** H_2O
hexane	C_6H_{14}	+	$9.5\ O_2$	→	$6\ CO_2$	+	$7\ H_2O$

   c. List three patterns you observe for the 6 balanced equations.

2. Examine the carbon compounds in the table below. All carbon compounds combust, except for CO_2.

Combustion Reactions of Carbon and Carbon-Containing Molecules							
methane	CH_4	+	$2\ O_2$	→	CO_2	+	$2\ H_2O$
methanol	CH_4O	+	**1.5** O_2	→	CO_2	+	$2\ H_2O$
carbon	C	+	$1\ O_2$	→	CO_2		
carbon monoxide	CO	+	$0.5\ O_2$	→	CO_2		
carbon dioxide	CO_2	+	$0\ O_2$	→	no reaction		

   a. Balance the equation for methanol in the table. Draw the structural formula for CH_4O, methanol.

   b. What patterns do you notice in the amount of oxygen that reacts?

   c. Do you think you can form CO_4? Why or why not?

3. The following table shows the equations for the potential reaction of different metals and salts with oxygen.

Combustion Reactions of Metals	
magnesium	$Mg + 0.5\ O_2 \rightarrow MgO$
magnesium oxide	$MgO + 0\ O_2 \rightarrow$ no reaction
magnesium chloride	$MgCl_2 + 0\ O_2 \rightarrow$ no reaction
titanium	$Ti + 1\ O_2 \rightarrow TiO_2$
titanium oxide	$TiO_2 + 0\ O_2 \rightarrow$ no reaction
titanium fluoride	$TiF_4 + 0\ O_2 \rightarrow$ no reaction

a. What patterns do you notice?
b. What is the charge on the magnesium atom in MgO?
c. What is the charge on titanium in TiO_2?
d. Why doesn't MgO combust?
e. Do you think that salts combust? Explain your thinking.

4. When carbon-containing molecules combust, a flame is visible. When metals combust, there is a glow, but no flame. Try to explain this observation. (Hint: Molecules enter the gas phase easily. Metals and metal oxides are solids.)

Making Sense:
What are the products of the combustion of carbon-containing molecules?
What are the products of the combustion of metals?
What are the products of the combustion of salts?

If you finish early…
Write a balanced equation for the reaction of $C_6H_{12}O_6$, glucose, with oxygen.

Making Sense Discussion (10–15 min)

Major goals: Students continue to build their understanding of combustion. They should come away from this discussion with an understanding of two major types of combustion reactions: combustion of carbon-containing molecules and combustion of metals. They should be able to identify the products and be able to identify patterns in the stoichiometry of the reactions. Relate a flame to the presences of glowing hot gases.

6. Discuss combustion equations.

Ask students to help you balance the combustion reactions as you write them on the board.

Discussion goals:

Assist students in writing balanced combustion equations. Discuss patterns in the stoichiometry of these equations.

Sample questions:

When ethanol, C_2H_6O, combusts, what is it reacting with? (oxygen)
What are the products of the combustion of ethanol?
How would you write the combustion of ethanol as a chemical equation?
($C_2H_6O + O_2 \rightarrow CO_2 + H_2O$)
Balance the equation.
When sodium combusts, what is it reacting with?
What are the products of the combustion of sodium?
How do you figure out the formula for sodium oxide?
How would you write the combustion of sodium as a chemical equation?
($Na + O_2 \rightarrow Na_2O$) Balance the equation.

Points to cover:

A combustion reaction is a reaction between a fuel and oxygen. In this lesson, we considered carbon-containing molecules and metals as fuels. When carbon-containing molecules combust, carbon dioxide and water are the products. When metals react with oxygen, metal oxides form. Some examples are given below.

Ethanol: $C_2H_6O + 3\ O_2 \rightarrow 2\ CO_2 + 3\ H_2O$

$2\ Na + 0.5\ O_2 \rightarrow Na_2O$ (or $4\ Na + O_2 \rightarrow 2\ Na_2O$)

7. Discuss why some reactions produce flames.

Discussion goals:

Help students to consider what causes a flame. Discuss the connection between flames and species in the gas phase.

Sample questions:

What are the products of combustion of carbon-containing molecules?
Are the products gases, liquids, or solids?
Do the reactants (carbon-containing molecules) enter the gas phase readily? Explain your thinking.
What do you think causes a flame?
What are the products of the combustion of metals?
Are the products of metal combustion gases, liquids, or solids?
Do metals enter the gas phase readily?
Why do you think is there no flame when a metal combusts?

Points to cover:

Each combustion reaction is actually a complex series of smaller steps. The fuel breaks down to smaller compounds and may move from the solid to the gas phase as it combusts. These gases are the cause of flames. Flames are simply highly heated gases giving off light.

One type of combustion reaction considered in this lesson is the combustion of carbon-containing molecules. The combustion products are gaseous carbon dioxide and water vapor. Since the carbon-containing molecules evaporate readily, the combustion reaction takes place in the gas phase. The flame consists of hot gas molecules moving rapidly. The flame has a visible color because some of these gas molecules are emitting light.

A second type of combustion reaction is the combustion of metals to form metal oxides as products. Both the metal reactants and the metal oxide products are solids. Since the metals do not enter the gas phase, the combustion reaction is confined to the surface of the solid. Consequently, a glow is observed, but no flame.

Check-in (5 min)

8. Introduce the Check-in exercise.

Write the following exercise on the board for students to complete individually.

- Pick a substance that combusts from the list below and write the balanced chemical reaction.

  Ar Al C CH_4O

9. Discuss the Check-in exercise.

Get a sense of the level of understanding by taking a vote, collecting students' work, or asking students to defend their choices.

Discussion goals:

Make sure students know how to write balanced chemical equations for combustion reactions.

10. Wrap-up

Assist the students in summarizing what was learned in the class.

- The products of the combustion of carbon-containing molecules are carbon dioxide and water.
- Flames are gases emitting light. Flames are the result of gases that are produced *during* a combustion reaction.
- In a combustion reaction, the longer the carbon chain in the fuel, the more oxygen it reacts with.
- The products of the combustion of metals are solid metal oxides. These reactions usually do not produce enough gases to support a flame.

Homework

11. Assign homework.

Homework – Investigation II – Lesson 3

1. Predict which substance will combust, 10 g of calcium, Ca, or 10 g of calcium chloride $CaCl_2$? Explain your reasoning. Write the balanced combustion reaction for the substance that combusts.
2. Propane (C_3H_8) is a fuel used in camp stoves.
   a. Draw the structural formula for propane.
   b. Write the balanced chemical reaction for the combustion of propane.
3. Hydrogen is a fuel used in the space shuttle.
   a. Write the balanced chemical reaction for the combustion of hydrogen.
   b. Write the Lewis dot structures for the reactants and product of this reaction.
4. When iron (Fe) rusts it reacts with oxygen.
   a. Balance the following reaction for the formation of rust.

   $$\_\_\_\_ Fe + \_\_\_\_ O_2 \rightarrow \_\_\_\_ Fe_2O_3$$

   b. What is the charge on the Fe ion? Explain your reasoning.
   c. Do you think rust is a combustion reaction? Explain your reasoning.
5. The chemical composition of sugar is $C_{12}H_{22}O_{11}$.
   a. What are the products when sugar is burned as fuel?
   b. Write the chemical reaction for the combustion of sugar.

Name: ____________________

All-A-Glow

Period: ____ Date: __________

Student Worksheet

Purpose: The goal of this lesson is to allow you to examine chemical equations that describe combustion reactions.

Answer the following questions:

1. Molecules containing carbon and hydrogen are called alkanes. Alkanes react with oxygen to produce carbon dioxide, water, and a fire.

   a. Draw the structural formulas for C_2H_6, ethane, and C_4H_{10}, butane.

   b. The reactions for methane, ethane, and hexane are balanced in the table. Balance the reactions for propane, butane, and pentane. (Solve for one unit of the fuel in each case.)

Combustion Reactions of Alkanes	
methane	CH_4 + $2\ O_2$ → CO_2 + $2\ H_2O$
ethane	C_2H_6 + $3.5\ O_2$ → $2\ CO_2$ + $3\ H_2O$
propane	C_3H_8 + O_2 → CO_2 + H_2O
butane	C_4H_{10} + O_2 → CO_2 + H_2O
pentane	C_5H_{12} + O_2 → CO_2 + H_2O
hexane	C_6H_{14} + $9.5\ O_2$ → $6\ CO_2$ + $7\ H_2O$

   c. List three patterns you observe for the six balanced equations.

2. Examine the carbon compounds shown in the table bellow. All carbon compounds combust, except for CO_2.

Combustion Reactions of Carbon and Carbon-Containing Molecules	
methane	CH_4 + $2\ O_2$ → CO_2 + $2\ H_2O$
methanol	CH_4O + O_2 → CO_2 + H_2O
carbon	C + $1\ O_2$ → CO_2
carbon monoxide	CO + $0.5\ O_2$ → CO_2
carbon dioxide	CO_2 + $0\ O_2$ → no reaction

a. Balance the equation for methanol in the table. Draw the structural formula for CH_4O, methanol.

b. What patterns do you notice in the amount of oxygen that reacts?

c. Do you think you can form CO_4? Why or why not?

3. This table shows the chemical equations for the potential reaction of different metals and salts with oxygen.

Combustion Reactions with Metals	
magnesium	$Mg + 0.5\ O_2 \rightarrow MgO$
magnesium oxide	$MgO + 0\ O_2 \rightarrow$ no reaction
magnesium chloride	$MgCl_2 + 0\ O_2 \rightarrow$ no reaction
titanium	$Ti + 1\ O_2 \rightarrow TiO_2$
titanium oxide	$TiO_2 + 0\ O_2 \rightarrow$ no reaction
titanium fluoride	$TiF_4 + 0\ O_2 \rightarrow$ no reaction

a. What patterns do you notice?

b. What is the charge on the magnesium atoms in MgO?

c. What is the charge on the titanium atoms in TiO_2?

d. Why doesn't MgO combust?

e. Do you think that salts combust? Explain your thinking.

4. When carbon-containing molecules combust, a flame is visible. When metals combust, there is a glow, but no flame. Try to explain this observation. (Hint: Molecules enter the gas phase easily. Metals and metal oxides are solids.)

Making Sense

What are the products of the combustion of carbon-containing molecules?
What are the products of the combustion of metals?
What are the products of the combustion of salts?

If you finish early…

Write a balanced equation for the reaction of $C_6H_{12}O_6$, glucose, with oxygen.

BEFORE CLASS…

LESSON 4 – Fuelish Choices

Key Ideas:
Carbon compounds make good fuels because they will readily combine with oxygen and release heat. The calorie content of a substance can be defined as the amount of heat that flows from that substance when it undergoes combustion. The calorie content of a substance can tell us something about how that substance performs as a fuel. In general, the more carbon atoms a compound has, the more energy is released when it burns.

What Takes Place:
Students are provided with a worksheet containing data that combines combustion reactions with calorie values for each reaction. Students look for patterns in the data and begin to compare "fuels." The calorie content provides information about how much energy may be available from the combustion of a substance. Students come up with some generalizations about which types of fuels transfer the most heat when they are burned. In addition students compare calorie output per mole versus calorie output per gram.

Materials:
- Student worksheet
- Fire Concept Map from Lesson I-6

Investigation II – Conditions for Change

LESSON 4 – Fuelish Choices

In this lesson students investigate the fuels involved in combustion. Their focus changes to one of examining and comparing substances in terms of their chemical formulas and energy output. They accomplish this by exploring combustion reactions in more detail. In addition students will compare calorie data to begin to make connections between energy output and chemical make-up. Finally, students will extend the Fire Chart by adding information about the fire triangle and fuels.

Exploring the Topic (5–10 min)

1. Introduce the ChemCatalyst exercise.

Write the following exercise on the board for students to complete individually. Write the three combustion equations on the board without the coefficients.

Standard automobiles use a mix of carbon-based compounds (high in octane) as fuel. The cars that race in the Indianapolis 500 use methanol as fuel. And top dragsters use nitromethane as fuel.

- Balance the equations for the combustion of these fuels.
- Why do you think they use different fuels for different types of driving?

(Below are the balanced chemical equations for these combustion reactions):

(octane) $2\ C_8H_{18} + 25\ O_2 \rightarrow 16\ CO_2 + 18\ H_2O$

(methanol) $2\ CH_4O + 3\ O_2 \rightarrow 2\ CO_2 + 4\ H_2O$

(nitromethane) $4\ CH_3NO_2 + 7\ O_2 \rightarrow 4\ CO_2 + 6\ H_2O + 4\ NO_2$

2. Discuss the ChemCatalyst exercise.

Use the discussion to get a sense of students' initial ideas.

Discussion goals:

Use the students' written responses to stimulate a discussion about the chemical composition of fuels.

Sample questions:

Why do you think octane (gasoline) is the most commonly used fuel in automobiles?

Why do you think they use different fuels for racing than for street vehicles?

Dragsters can accelerate to 330 mph in four seconds. What do you think the fuel has to do with the speed of the vehicle?

What things do the three chemical equations have in common? (All react with oxygen; all result in carbon dioxide and water as products.)
What are the major differences between the fuels? (number of carbon and hydrogen atoms, the presence of an oxygen atom in the methanol, and two oxygen atoms in the nitromethane, the presence of a nitrogen atom)
What are the major differences between the combustion reactions? (different numbers of moles of oxygen, different number of moles of products)

3. Explain the purpose of today's activity.

If you wish you can write the main question on the board.

Points to cover:
Tell students they will be gathering information to answer the question: "How do different fuels compare to one another?"

Activity – Fuelish Choices (15 min)

4. Introduce the activity. (Worksheet)

Pass out the worksheet. Allow students to work in pairs.

The table below shows the chemical equations associated with the combustion of a variety of fuels. In addition, the table shows the calories of heat released by the combustion of a mole of each substance.

Combustion Reactions			
Substance	**Chemical Formula**	**Energy (cal/mole)**	**Chemical Reaction**
Octane	C_8H_{18} (l)	1,300,000	$2\ C_8H_{18} + 25\ O_2 \rightarrow 16\ CO_2 + 18\ H_2O$
Hexane	C_6H_{14} (l)	995,000	$2\ C_6H_{14} + 19\ O_2 \rightarrow 12\ CO_2 + 14\ H_2O$
Hexanol	$C_6H_{14}O$ (l)	951,000	$C_6H_{14}O + 9\ O_2 \rightarrow 6\ CO_2 + 7\ H_2O$
Butane	C_4H_{10} (l)	687,000	$2\ C_4H_{10} + 13\ O_2 \rightarrow 8\ CO_2 + 10\ H_2O$
Butanol	$C_4H_{10}O$ (l)	638,000	$C_4H_{10}O + 6\ O_2 \rightarrow 4\ CO_2 + 5\ H_2O$
Ethane	C_2H_6 (g)	373,000	$2\ C_2H_6 + 7\ O_2 \rightarrow 4\ CO_2 + 6\ H_2O$
Ethanol	C_2H_6O (l)	327,000	$C_2H_6O + 3\ O_2 \rightarrow 2\ CO_2 + 3\ H_2O$
Methane	CH_4 (g)	213,000	$CH_4 + 2\ O_2 \rightarrow CO_2 + 2\ H_2O$
Methanol	CH_4O (l)	174,000	$2\ CH_4O + 3\ O_2 \rightarrow 2\ CO_2 + 4\ H_2O$

Nitromethane	$CH_3NO_2(l)$	175,000	$4\ CH_3NO_2 + 7\ O_2 \rightarrow 4\ CO_2 + 6\ H_2O + 4\ NO_2$
Hydrogen	H_2 (g)	58,000	$2\ H_2 + O_2 \rightarrow 2\ H_2O$

Use the table above to answer the following questions:

1. Which fuel has the highest output of energy in calories per mole of fuel? (octane)
2. Which fuel has the lowest output of energy in calories per mole of fuel? (hydrogen)
3. What happens to the energy output as carbon atoms are added to the formula of the fuel molecule? (Energy output increases as the carbon chain gets bigger.)
4. What happens to the energy output when oxygen atoms are added to the formula of the fuel molecule? (Energy output decreases slightly with the addition of an oxygen atom to the molecule.)
5. According to the above chart, name or describe a fuel that would be even better than any of the fuels listed. Explain your reasoning. (A fuel with more carbons should produce more energy – nonane.)
6. What kind of energy output would you expect for the combustion of a mole of propane, C_3H_8? Explain your reasoning. (Propane should produce between ethane and butane's values, because it has three carbon atoms and eight hydrogen atoms.)
7. Write the chemical equation showing the combustion of propane, C_3H_8. Make sure it is balanced. ($C_3H_8 + 5\ O_2 \rightarrow 3\ CO_2 + 4\ H_2O$)
8. How do the fuels mentioned in the ChemCatalyst compare to each other? (Octane produces about 9 times more energy per mole than the other fuels, methanol and nitromethane are about the same.)
9. What happens to the amount of oxygen that is needed to combust with the fuel as the number of carbon atoms increases in the chemical formula? (Amount of oxygen that is needed increases as the carbon atoms increase.)

Complete the following table:

Substance	Chemical Formula	Energy kcal/mol	Mol. Wt. g/mol	Energy kcal/gram
Octane	C_8H_{18}	1300	114	11.4
Hexane	C_6H_{14}	995	86	11.5
Hexanol	$C_6H_{14}O$	**951**	**102**	**9.3**
Butane	C_4H_{10}	**687**	58	**11.8**
Butanol	$C_4H_{10}O$	638	74	**8.6**
Ethane	C_2H_6	373	**30**	**12.4**
Ethanol	C_2H_6O	**327**	46	**7.1**

Methane	CH_4	213	**16**	**13.3**
Methanol	CH_4O	**174**	32	5.4
Hydrogen	H_2	58	**2**	**29**
Nitromethane	CH_3NO_2	**175**	61	**2.9**

10. List the top six fuels in terms of the amount of energy released per gram of substance combusted. (hydrogen, methane, ethane, butane, hexane, and octane)
7. Which provides more energy, 100 grams of octane, 100 grams of methanol, or 100 grams of hydrogen? Which provides the least energy? (100 grams of hydrogen provides 2900 kcal of energy, 100 grams of methanol provides 540 kcal of energy, 100 grams of octane provides 1140 kcal.)

Making sense:
Do you think the best fuel is always the one that has the greatest energy output in calories per mole? Explain your reasoning.

If you finish early...
Hydrogen is used as a rocket fuel. How many grams of octane would you need to produce the same amount of energy as 100,000 grams of hydrogen?

Making Sense Discussion (10–15 min)

Major goals: Students begin to consider what makes a good fuel in this lesson. They examine molecules with short and long carbon atom chains, and molecules with and without oxygen atoms. Energy output in kcal/mol is compared with kcal/g. Students should understand that there are any number of factors that go into deciding whether a substance is a good fuel. The discussion ends by adding the fire triangle and fuels to the Fire Chart constructed at the end of Investigation I.

5. Discuss and compare fuels. (Transparency)

Display the transparency with the second table from the worksheet for use during the discussion.

Discussion goals:
Clarify the main points that emerged from today's activity regarding fuels.

Sample questions:
Which substances had the greatest output of energy in kcal per mole? (octane, carbon compounds with long chains)
What, if any, generalizations can you make about the substances that produced the greatest heat transfer?

Which substances had the greatest output of energy in kcal per gram? (Hydrogen was greatest, then came smaller carbon compounds – reverse order of the previous question.)

Can you make any generalizations about these substances? (They are smaller compounds with lower mass. They don't require as much oxygen to combust.)

What substances make good fuels, according to today's activity? What is your reasoning? (Small carbon compounds without oxygen in their formulas generally make good fuels. Compounds that do not require so much oxygen to combine with.)

Points to cover:
Molecular covalent compounds, especially carbon compounds, make good fuels. They combine readily with oxygen to produce carbon dioxide and water. As the number of carbon atoms in a compound increases, it appears that the energy output also increases accordingly. When oxygen atoms are added to the formulas, we see a drop in energy output. All in all, alkanes and alcohols make very good fuels.

However, the energy output of each substance is just one consideration in rating fuels. When we compare octane, methanol, and nitromethane in our tables we find that octane has nine times the output of energy in kcal per mole of fuel. Methanol and nitromethane are used in racecars to produce incredible speeds and massive amounts of horsepower.

One consideration in comparing fuels, in addition to the amount of heat transferred, is how fast the heat is produced. You may have noticed that larger carbon compounds require massive amounts of oxygen (examine the equations). Trying to create an engine that will provide enough oxygen for the particular fuel can be a challenge. With methanol and nitromethane, it is possible to burn a lot more fuel in a shorter amount of time because these fuels don't need as much oxygen. So, while longer carbon chains appear to produce more energy, it may be more difficult to get that energy out because these compounds require so much oxygen in order to combust fully. For octane to provide the same energy output as methanol it would take a larger gas tank, a heavier car, and a larger engine. that provides a lot more oxygen to the fuel.

The results of the activity show us that some fuels may produce more energy per mole, but actually produce less energy per gram. This becomes an issue when one is worried about the weight of a fuel or the amount of space it might take up. So apparently, bigger is not always better when it comes to fuels. Obviously hydrogen is an extremely lightweight fuel compared to carbon compounds. It produces much more energy per gram than any other fuel in our table. And octane turns out to be the best fuel for the purposes of our daily driving needs at present.

We have yet to consider the energy output of metals that combust. We will examine them in a later lesson.

6. Introduce the kilocalorie and the kiloJoule.

Points to cover:

We have defined a calorie as a unit of heat measurement. A calorie is defined based on heating water: 1 calorie is needed to raise the temperature of 1 gram of water by 1 degree centigrade. A food Calorie (with a big "C") is 1000 times the calories (with a small "c") used by chemists.

The calories used by chemists represent a very small amount of heat. In general, when you burn several grams of a substance, about 1000 calories of heat is transferred. Chemists use the prefix "kilo" to indicate 1000 times. Thus, 1 kilocalorie (abbreviated as 1 kcal) is equal to 1000 calories and is equal to a food Calorie.

The kcal is a good unit to use because it is related to heating water. However, it is an older unit. The metric unit used by scientists is the kiloJoule or kJ. A Joule is a unit of heat that is 4.184 times as large as a calorie. Thus, 1 kJ = 4.184 kcal. We will continue to use the kcal, but you will be given problems for homework to practice converting between the older unit, kcal, to the newer unit, kJ.

kilocalories or kcal: 1 kcal is equal to 1000 calories. It is also equal to 1 food Calorie

kiloJoule or kJ: 1 kJ is equal to 4.184 kcal. Joules are the metric units in common use by scientists.

7. Add to the Fire Map. (Butcher paper)

Place the butcher paper Fire Map on the wall and use a marking pen to add to the chart. Add information about fuels to the left side of the Fire Map.

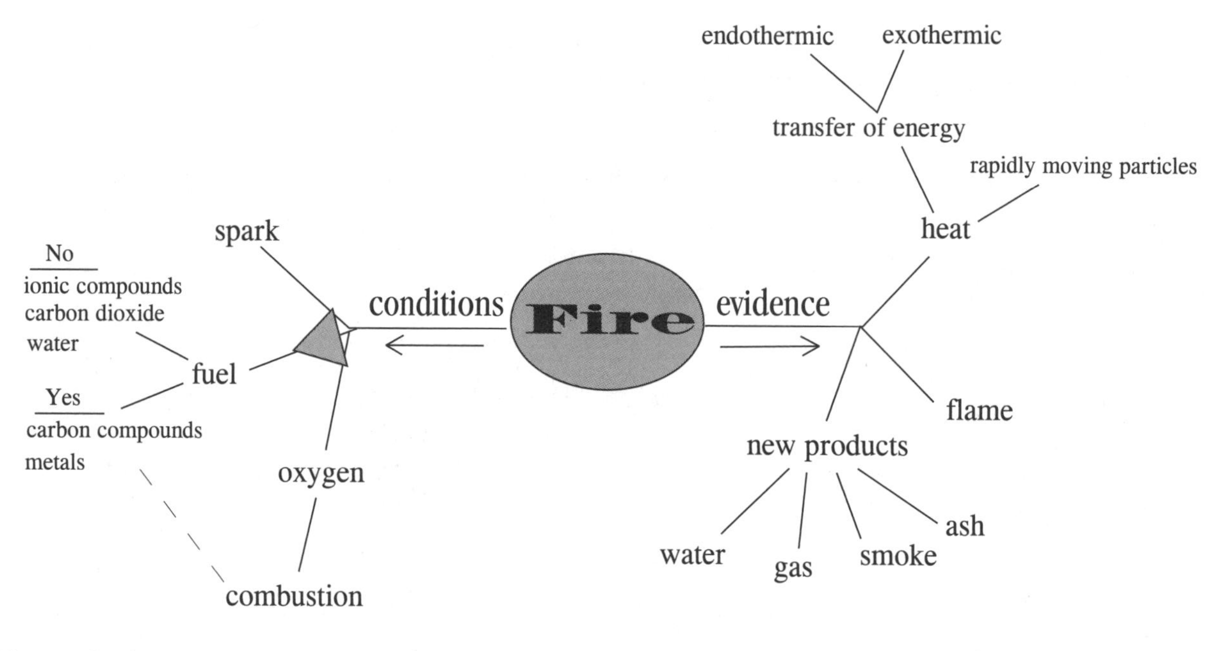

Check-in (5 min)

8. Introduce the Check-in exercise.

Write the following exercise on the board for students to complete individually.

- Which molecule of the three listed below would you expect to release the most energy per mole of fuel combusted? What is your reasoning?

propane, C_3H_8 propanol, C_3H_8O pentane, C_5H_{12}

9. Discuss the Check-in exercise.

Get a sense of the level of understanding by taking a vote, collecting students' work, or asking students to defend their choices.

Discussion goals:

Make sure students understand the relationship between chemical make-up and energy output in calories, during combustion.

Sample questions:

Which substance has the greatest output of energy in kcal per mole?
How does energy output depend on the number of carbon atoms?
How does energy output depend on the number of oxygen atoms?

10. Wrap-up

Assist the students in summarizing what was learned in the class.

- Substances consisting mostly of carbon and hydrogen atoms are good fuels.
- Trends show that the larger the carbon compound, the more energy is released per mole of fuel when that compound combusts.

- Molecules without oxygen atoms tend to release more energy than comparable molecules that contain oxygen (e.g., $CH_4 > CH_3OH$).
- The amount of calories released during combustion is dependent on the size of the molecule.
- Chemists use kJoules as a unit of energy. One kcal = 4.184 kJoules.

Homework

11. Assign homework.

Use the homework provided with the curriculum or assign your own.

Homework – Investigation II – Lesson 4

1. Which would provide a greater output of energy – 10 molecules of hexanol, 10 molecules of hexane, or 10 molecules of ethane. Explain your reasoning.
2. Chemists prefer to work in units called joules or kiloJoules, rather than calories or kilocalories. One kcal = 4.184 kJoules. Convert the units in the following table from kcal to kJoules.

Substance	Chemical Formula	Energy kcal/mol	Energy kJoules/mol	Energy kcal/gram	Energy kJoules/gram
Octane	C_8H_{18}	1300		11.4	
Hexane	C_6H_{14}	995		11.5	
Hexanol	$C_6H_{14}O$	951		9.3	
Ethane	C_2H_6	373		12.4	
Ethanol	C_2H_6O	327		7.1	
Methane	CH_4	213		13.3	
Methanol	CH_4O	174		5.4	
Hydrogen	H_2	58		29	
Nitromethane	CH_3NO_2	175		2.9	

3. How many moles of oxygen unite with one mole of each of the following fuels?

$$2\,C_2H_6 + 7\,O_2 \rightarrow 4\,CO_2 + 6\,H_2O$$

$$C_6H_{14}O + 9\,O_2 \rightarrow 6\,CO_2 + 7\,H_2O$$

$$4\,CH_3NO_2 + 7\,O_2 \rightarrow 4\,CO_2 + 6\,H_2O + 4\,NO_2$$

$$2\,C_8H_{18} + 25\,O_2 \rightarrow 16\,CO_2 + 18\,H_2O$$

4. Which fuel from question three is the most efficient in terms of requiring less oxygen per mole of fuel to burn? Rank the fuels in terms of oxygen consumption.
5. If you had a cup of methane and a cup of ethanol, which do you think would provide more energy when combusted? What is your reasoning?

Fuelish Choices

Substance	Chemical Formula	Energy kcal/mol	Mol. Wt. g/mol	Energy kcal/gram
Octane	C_8H_{18}	1300	114	11.4
Hexane	C_6H_{14}	995	86	11.5
Hexanol	$C_6H_{14}O$	**951**	**102**	**9.3**
Butane	C_4H_{10}	**687**	58	**11.8**
Butanol	$C_4H_{10}O$	638	74	**8.6**
Ethane	C_2H_6	373	**30**	**12.4**
Ethanol	C_2H_6O	**327**	46	**7.1**
Methane	CH_4	213	**16**	**13.3**
Methanol	CH_4O	**174**	32	5.4
Hydrogen	H_2	58	**2**	**29**
Nitromethane	CH_3NO_2	**175**	61	**2.9**

Transparency

Student Worksheet

Fuelish Choices

Name: ______________________

Period: ____ Date: ____________

Purpose: In this activity, you will compare fuels to one another by examining their combustion reactions and calorie output.

The table below shows the chemical equations associated with the combustion of a variety of fuels. In addition, the table shows the calories of heat released by the combustion of one mole of each substance.

Combustion Reactions			
Substance	**Chemical Formula**	**Energy (cal/mole)**	**Chemical Reaction**
Octane	C_8H_{18} (l)	1,300,000	$2\ C_8H_{18} + 25\ O_2 \rightarrow 16\ CO_2 + 18\ H_2O$
Hexane	C_6H_{14} (l)	995,000	$2\ C_6H_{14} + 19\ O_2 \rightarrow 12\ CO_2 + 14\ H_2O$
Hexanol	$C_6H_{14}O$ (l)	951,000	$2\ C_6H_{14}O + 18O_2 \rightarrow 12\ CO_2 + 14\ H_2O$
Butane	C_4H_{10} (l)	687,000	$2\ C_4H_{10} + 13\ O_2 \rightarrow 8\ CO_2 + 10\ H_2O$
Butanol	$C_4H_{10}O$ (l)	638,000	$C_4H_{10}O + 6\ O_2 \rightarrow 4\ CO_2 + 5\ H_2O$
Ethane	C_2H_6 (g)	373,000	$2\ C_2H_6 + 7\ O_2 \rightarrow 4\ CO_2 + 6\ H_2O$
Ethanol	C_2H_6O (l)	327,000	$C_2H_6O + 3\ O_2 \rightarrow 2\ CO_2 + 3\ H_2O$
Methane	CH_4 (g)	213,000	$CH_4 + 2\ O_2 \rightarrow CO_2 + 2\ H_2O$
Methanol	CH_4O (l)	174,000	$2\ CH_4O + 3\ O_2 \rightarrow 2\ CO_2 + 4\ H_2O$
Nitromethane	CH_3NO_2 (l)	175,000	$4\ CH_3NO_2 + 7\ O_2 \rightarrow 4\ CO_2 + 6\ H_2O + 4\ NO_2$
Hydrogen	H_2 (g)	58,000	$2\ H_2 + O_2 \rightarrow 2\ H_2O$

Use the table above to answer the following questions:

1. Which fuel has the highest output of energy in calories per mole of fuel?
2. Which fuel has the lowest output of energy in calories per mole of fuel?
3. What happens to the energy output as carbon atoms are added to the formula of the fuel molecule?
4. What happens to the energy output when oxygen atoms are added to the formula of the fuel molecule?
5. According to the above chart, name or describe a fuel that would be even better than any of the fuels listed. Explain your reasoning.
6. What kind of energy output would you expect for the combustion of a mole of propane, C_3H_8? Explain your reasoning.

7. Write the chemical equation showing the combustion of propane, C_3H_8. Make sure it is balanced.

8. How do the fuels mentioned in the ChemCatalyst compare to each other?

9. What happens to the amount of oxygen that is needed to combust with the fuel as the number of carbon atoms increases in the chemical formula?

Complete the following table:

Substance	Chemical Formula	Energy kcal/mol	Mol. Wt. g/mol	Energy kcal/gram
Octane	C_8H_{18}	1,300	114	11.4
Hexane	C_6H_{14}	995	86	11.5
Hexanol	$C_6H_{14}O$			
Butane	C_4H_{10}		58	
Butanol	$C_4H_{10}O$	638	74	
Ethane	C_2H_6	373		
Ethanol	C_2H_6O		46	
Methane	CH_4	213		
Methanol	CH_4O		32	5.4
Hydrogen	H_2	58		
Nitromethane	CH_3NO_2		61	

10. List the top six fuels in terms of the amount of energy released per gram of substance combusted.

11. Which provides more energy, 100 grams of octane, 100 grams of methanol, or 100 grams of hydrogen? Which provides the least energy?

Making sense:
Do you think the best fuel is the one that has the greatest energy output in calories per mole? Explain your reasoning.

If you finish early...
Hydrogen is used as a rocket fuel. How many grams of octane would you need to produce the same amount of energy as 100,000 grams of hydrogen?

BEFORE CLASS…

LESSON 5 – Sparklers

Key Ideas:
Oxygen, fuel, and heat are the three legs of the fire triangle. Heat (sometimes referred to as a spark) is necessary to get a combustion reaction started. Combustion reactions of metals with oxygen produce metal oxides. When the combustion of various metals is used to heat certain metal salts, a colorful sparkler can be produced.

What Takes Place:
In this laboratory activity students will follow a recipe to create sparklers similar to those used during holiday celebrations. As part of their preparation, the sparklers must be dried, so they will not be tested until the following lesson. After the sparklers have been assembled students will complete a short worksheet.

Materials (per class of 32 students):

- Student worksheet
- 16 g cornstarch
- wire hangers cut into 8–10 inch lengths (32 pieces)
- 40 mL water
- 25 g Fe powder
- 2 g Mg powder
- 6 g Al powder
- 4 g Cu powder
- 16 g $KClO_3$, potassium chlorate
- 65 g $Ba(NO_3)_2$, barium nitrate
- 65 g $Sr(NO_3)_2$, strontium nitrate
- 8 watch glasses
- 2 large beakers
- 8 hot plates
- 8 balances
- 8 surgical gloves

SAFETY NOTE: Although sparklers are legal in most states, they are banned in some states and counties. Check with your local fire marshal to determine whether you can do this activity with your class.

Investigation II – Conditions for Change

LESSON 5 – Sparklers

In this activity students complete a laboratory procedure that results in the creation of several different sparklers, similar to those used for celebrations. The newly created sparklers must be dried in an oven for several hours. Thus the creation of the sparklers occurs on one day and the testing and processing of them on another day. After the sparklers are created and placed in an appropriate container for drying by the instructor, students must finish a worksheet. The focus of this lesson is two-pronged. First it allows students to explore the combustion of metals. Second, this lesson sets up an introduction to the concept of a fourth condition necessary for fire – a chemical chain reaction.

Exploring the Topic (5–10 min)

1. Introduce the ChemCatalyst exercise.

Write the following exercise on the board for students to complete individually.

- I have several matches, a large tree trunk from a fallen tree, and plenty of oxygen in the atmosphere. Nevertheless, I cannot get the tree trunk to burn using just a lit match. If I have all three legs of the fire triangle, why is it difficult to make a fire?

2. Discuss the ChemCatalyst exercise.

Use the discussion to get a sense of students' initial ideas.

Discussion goals:

Use the students' written responses to stimulate a discussion about what conditions will sustain a fire.

Sample questions:

Why can't you get a tree trunk to burn with just a couple of matches?
What could you do to get the trunk to burn?
What are you adding to the fuel, oxygen, and spark in the last question?
If you had to describe another condition for fire, beyond the fire triangle, what would it be?

Among other things, students may say chop the wood into pieces (this would increase surface area in contact with oxygen) or add lighter fluid or pile dry leaves around it (which in effect would provide hotter and more long-lasting heat to light the fire). Students may share stories about how hard it is to start a campfire, and how frustrating it is when it goes out after a few minutes. On the other hand, some fires light very quickly and grow rapidly (e.g., a brush fire, or a silo fire). In today's lesson we will be trying to get at the idea of a chain reaction – energy needed to keep the fire going and growing.

3. Explain the purpose of today's activity.

If you wish you can write the main question on the board.

Points to cover:
Tell students they will be gathering information to answer the question: "What keeps a combustion reaction going?"

Activity – Sparklers (15 min)

4. Introduce the activity. (Worksheet)

Pass out the worksheet and go over the directions for the lab. Ask students to work in teams of four on the lab portion of the class. Remind students to wear goggles at all times during lab activities. After creating their sparklers they should work individually on the remainder of their worksheets.

Safety Note: Remember to wear goggles during today's lab.

Materials: (per team of four students)
2 g cornstarch
wire hangers cut into 8–10 inch lengths
5.0 mL water
3.3 g Fe powder
0.2 g Mg powder
0.7 g Al powder
0.4 g Cu powder
2.0 g $KClO_3$, potassium chlorate
8.3 g $Ba(NO_3)_2$, barium nitrate
8.3 g $Sr(NO_3)_2$, strontium nitrate (optional / half the class?)
watch glass
hot plate
stirring rod
goggles
2 large beakers
masking tape
surgical gloves

Directions:
Note: Two team members should prepare the starch mixture while the other two weigh out the different powders.

1. Find the mass of your watch glass and record it below. (You will be using the watch glass to weigh out all the different powders.)
2. Use the watch glass and balance to measure out 2 grams of cornstarch.
3. Measure 5.0 mL of water in a graduated cylinder. Pour the water and cornstarch into a beaker and stir well. There should be no lumps.
4. Heat the mixture, stirring constantly, until it starts to thicken. As soon as it begins to thickens, remove it from the heat. CONTINUE TO STIR the starch until it becomes like a paste.
5. Measure out each of the other ingredients (see chart below). Place the powders together in a dry beaker until the starch mixture is ready.
6. Once the starch mixture is like toothpaste, add the dry ingredients: 3.3 g Fe powder, 0.2 g Mg powder, 0.7 g Al powder, 2.0 g $KClO_3$, and 8.3 g $Ba(NO_3)_2$. Mix well.

7. Put on a glove. Smear the paste around a wire or stick. Leave at least 3 inches free at one end so that the sparkler can be held safely.
8. Use a piece of masking tape to label your sparklers so that you can recover them for testing later. Your instructor will dry your sparklers in an oven at a low temperature for several hours.
9. Optional: Repeat the above directions a second time, to make a second sparkler, substituting 8.3 g $Sr(NO_3)_2$ for the $Ba(NO_3)_2$.

Substance	Mass of watch glass + powder	(minus) Mass of watch glass	(equals) Mass of powder needed
Starch			2.0 g
Iron powder (Fe)			3.3 g
Copper powder (Cu)			0.4 g
Magnesium powder (Mg)			0.2 g
Aluminum powder (Al)			0.7 g
Potassium chlorate ($KClO_3$)			2.0 g
Barium nitrate ($Ba(NO_3)_2$)			8.3 g

Answer the following questions:

1. Predict what you will see when you light your sparkler. (Answers will vary.)
2. Is lighting a sparkler an example of combustion? Explain your reasoning. (Yes, because metals are combining with oxygen to form metal oxides and these reactions produce heat and light.)
3. List at least two combustion equations that you might expect to see using the above ingredients. Make sure to balance your equations.

   ($2\,Mg + O_2 \rightarrow 2\,MgO$, $4\,Al + 3\,O_2 \rightarrow 2\,Al_2O_3$, $2\,Fe + O_2 \rightarrow 2\,FeO$, $4\,Fe + O_2 \rightarrow 2\,Fe_2O_3$, $2\,Cu + O_2 \rightarrow 2\,CuO$)
4. What ionic compounds are used in this procedure? What role do you think the ionic compounds play in the sparkler chemistry? (potassium chlorate and barium nitrate, $KClO_3$, $Ba(NO_3)_2$. Answers will vary – provide oxygen for combustion, cause the colored light of the sparkler, not sure.)
5. Explain how you think your sparkler gives off light. (Answers will vary. Students will be speculating to a certain extent. Some light comes from combustion, some just from heating, which causes the excitation of electrons to different energy levels.)

Making sense:

Why does a sparkler keep going after you light it? Why doesn't it go out? (Answers will vary. Basically, a chain reaction is set up. The heat from the combustion of the first portion of the sparkler gets the next portion of the sparkler going, and so on.)

If you finish early...
You can have the three legs of the fire triangle, but still not have combustion. Give an example of this situation. (Many examples. Can heat lots of fuels and they will not combust. However, an open flame will often start combustion. Wet fuels will not burn. Large pieces of fuel will have difficulty burning.)

Note that the emphasis of these questions is on soliciting the students' ideas and explanations. Thus, it is more important for students to support their ideas with reasonable explanations, hunches, and evidence than it is for them to be "right."

Making Sense Discussion (10–15 min)

Major goals: This Making Sense Discussion will be limited because of the time constraints of the lab activity. If there is time allow students to share their experience of creating their sparklers. You may wish to focus on one or more of the speculative questions on the worksheet. If students do not have time to complete the worksheet in class, it should be assigned for homework.

5. Discuss the creation and burning of sparklers.

Discussion goals:
Assist students in sharing their ideas about the combustion of sparklers.

Sample questions:
Did you encounter any difficulties in the creation of your sparkler? Explain.
What do you think you will see when you light your sparkler?
What color flame or sparks do you expect to see from your sparkler? What is your reasoning?
What substances do you think will be (and will not be) combusting when you light your sparkler? Explain your reasoning.
What do you need to do to get a sparkler started? To keep it going?
Why do you need to let the sparklers dry overnight before trying to ignite them?

Check-in (5 min)

6. No Check-in for this lesson.

7. Wrap-up

Assist the students in summarizing what was learned in the class.

- The combustion of various metals can be used to create a colorful sparkler.
- There appears to be another condition necessary for fire, beyond the three legs of the fire triangle.

Homework

8. Assign homework.

No homework provided for this lesson.

Sparklers

Name: ____________________

Period: ____ Date: ___________

Purpose: In this lesson you will create sparklers using several metals and several ionic compounds. **Safety Note:** Remember to wear goggles during today's lab.

Materials: (per team of four students)

2 g cornstarch
5.0 mL water
3.3 g Fe powder
0.2 g Mg powder
0.7 g Al powder
0.4 g Cu powder
2.0 g $KClO_3$, potassium chlorate
8.3 g $Ba(NO_3)_2$, barium nitrate
8.3 g $Sr(NO_3)_2$, strontium nitrate (optional / half the class?)

wire hangers cut into 8–10 inch lengths
watch glass
hot plate
stirring rod
goggles
2 large beakers
masking tape
surgical gloves

Directions:

Note: Two team members should prepare the starch mixture while the other two weigh out the different powders.

1. Find the mass of your watch glass and record it below. (You will be using it to weigh out all the different powders.)
2. Use the watch glass and balance to measure out 2 grams of cornstarch.
3. Measure 5.0 mL of water in a graduated cylinder. Pour the water and cornstarch into a beaker and stir well. There should be no lumps.
4. Heat the mixture, stirring constantly, until it starts to thicken. As soon as it begins to thickens, remove it from the heat. CONTINUE TO STIR the starch until it becomes like a paste.
5. Measure out each of the other ingredients (see chart below). Once you have weighed out the powders, place them together in a dry beaker until the starch mixture is ready.
6. Once the starch mixture is like toothpaste, add the dry ingredients: 3.3 g Fe powder, 0.2 g Mg powder, 0.7 g Al powder, 2.0 g $KClO_3$, and 8.3 g $Ba(NO_3)_2$. Mix well.
7. Put on a glove. Smear the paste around a wire or stick. Leave at least 3 inches free at one end so that the sparkler can be held safely.
8. Use a piece of masking tape to label your sparklers so that you can recover them for testing later. Your instructor will dry your sparklers in an oven at a low temperature for several hours.
9. Optional: Repeat the above directions a second time, to make a second sparkler. This time substitute 8.3 g $Sr(NO_3)_2$ for the $Ba(NO_3)_2$.

Substance	Mass of watch glass + powder	(minus) Mass of watch glass	(equals) Mass of powder needed
Starch			2.0 g
Iron powder (Fe)			3.3 g
Copper powder (Cu)			0.4 g
Magnesium powder (Mg)			0.2 g
Aluminum powder (Al)			0.7 g
Potassium chlorate ($KClO_3$)			2.0 g
Barium nitrate ($Ba(NO_3)_2$)			8.3 g

Answer the following questions:

1. Predict what you will see when you light your sparkler.

2. Is lighting a sparkler an example of combustion? Explain your reasoning.

3. List at least two combustion equations that you might expect to see using the above ingredients. Make sure to balance your equations.

4. What ionic compounds are used in this procedure? What role do you think the ionic compounds play in the sparkler chemistry?

5. Explain how you think your sparkler gives off light.

Making sense:

Why does a sparkler keep going after you light it? Why doesn't it go out?

If you finish early...

You can have the three legs of the fire triangle, but still not have combustion. Give an example of this situation.

BEFORE CLASS…

LESSON 6 – Kablooie!

Key Ideas:
Explosions are described as the effect that occurs when there is a rapid expansion of gases. The popping of a balloon with a pin results in a type of explosion. Thus, an explosion is not always associated with a fire event. However, explosions can sometimes accompany combustion, and can occur when combustion takes place extremely rapidly. A fire will not burn unless there is a sustained chemical chain reaction to support it.

What Takes Place:
Students begin the class by burning the sparklers they assembled in the previous lesson. Students then observe several demonstrations dealing with explosions. Students record their observations, answer a few questions, and create a paper "fire tetrahedron." Finally, the Fire Concept Map is updated and summarized.

Set-up: Before class you should do some preparation for your demonstrations. You should blow up one balloon and tie it off. You will need to punch a hole on the top and bottom of an egg, blow out the contents, rinse the inside of the eggshell with water, and allow the shell to dry (the eggshell will by used to show the combustion of methane). Finally, you should cut out and create a 3-dimensional paper fire tetrahedron. You may also wish to "load" the surgical tubing with flour before class.

Materials:
- Student worksheet
- baking flour
- surgical tubing or long pipette
- funnel
- candle or Bunsen burner
- matches
- intact eggshell with the contents blown out
- natural gas used for Bunsen burners (to put inside the eggshell)
- string
- ringstand
- balloon containing air
- pushpin
- candle on a stick or other way of igniting balloon from a distance
- Fire Concept Map on butcher paper
- scissors
- Elmer's glue or glue sticks

Investigation II – Conditions for Change

LESSON 6 – Kablooie!

There are two main, but overlapping, concepts introduced during this lesson: the fire tetrahedron and the chemistry of explosions. Students begin this lesson by burning and observing the sparklers they created in the previous lesson. The sparklers lead into the introduction of a fourth condition necessary for fire – a sustained chemical chain reaction. Students will observe several demonstrations by the instructor that show how surface area can influence the rate of a reaction and result in explosions.

Exploring the Topic (5–10 min)

1. Introduce the ChemCatalyst exercise.

Write the following exercise on the board for students to complete individually.

- What is an explosion?
- What causes explosions?
- Have you ever seen or experienced an explosion? Explain.

2. Discuss the ChemCatalyst exercise.

Use the discussion to get a sense of students' initial ideas.

Discussion goals:
Use the students' written responses to stimulate a discussion about explosions.

Sample questions:
How would you define an explosion?
What qualities does an explosion have?
Have you ever experienced an explosion? What was it?
Why do you think explosions are dangerous?
What causes explosions?
What do explosions have to do with fire or combustion?

3. Explain the purpose of today's activity.

If you wish you can write the main question on the board.

Points to cover:
Tell students they will be observing several combustion reactions and gathering information to answer the question: "What does the rate of a combustion reaction have to do with fire?"

Activity – Kablooie! (15 min)

4. Test the students' sparklers. (Worksheet)

Allow students to collect their sparklers from the previous class. Pass out worksheets and ask students to test and observe their sparklers.

SAFETY NOTE: Goggles should be worn by all. The sparklers will emit sparks. You may wish to protect your skin. In addition, those testing the sparklers should not be wearing loose or highly flammable clothing.

Instructions:

1. Hold your sparkler by the end that is bare metal.
2. Point your sparkler away from others and away from combustible materials.
3. Light a match and hold it to the end of your sparkler until it begins to burn.
4. Observe your sparkler until it stops burning. The charred wire may be hot. Dispose of your sparkler properly as instructed by your teacher.

5. Complete the explosion demonstrations.

Students will observe the following three demonstrations. You may wish to have volunteers assist you. Students should complete their worksheets after observing the three demonstrations.

Suggested demonstrations:

DEMO 1 – Party balloon

Materials:

balloon filled with air
pushpin

Have a balloon on hand that has been created by breathing into it and tying it off. Ask students to predict what will happen when you stick the balloon with a pin. Ask them what they will observe or experience. Then, go ahead and puncture the balloon with a pin.

DEMO 2 – Flour Mountain and Breath of Fire

Materials:

candle or Bunsen burner
match
plastic tubing
fine flour – cake flour or baking flour (optional: lycopodium powder)
funnel that fits inside plastic tubing
small metal pan or can lid

Flour Mountain: Place several tablespoons of flour in the shallow metal pan. There should be enough flour for students to see clearly from a distance. Light a match and apply the match to the little mountain of flour. The flour may glow or burn a tiny bit when the match is applied. However, the flame quickly extinguishes when the match is removed from direct contact. The flour alone does not support a flame after the match is gone.

Breath of Fire: This demonstration may be done with surgical tubing, in which case the flour is blown across the flame. Alternatively, a pipette may be filled with a small amount of flour. The bulb on the pipette can be used to propel the flour across the flame.

Instructions: Insert flour into the surgical tube by fitting the funnel into one end of the surgical tubing and pouring several tablespoons of flour into the funnel. Light the candle (or Bunsen burner). Place the candle or burner on a lab bench that is cleared of any papers or flammable objects. Hold the surgical tubing so that both ends are suspended above the middle. Blow into one end of the tubing so that the flour is essentially blown across and through the flame. A large fireball should result. Therefore, the flour should not be blown in the direction of any students or flammable substances.

DEMO **3 – Methane-filled eggshell**

Materials:
candle on a stick (to hold at a distance)
matches
eggshell with the contents blown out, rinsed on the inside with water, and dried
pipette with a narrow opening
tubing to attach the pipette to the natural gas outlet
goggles

Instructions: Prepare the eggshell before class. Punch a small hole in the top and bottom. Blow out the contents. Rinse the eggshell on the inside with water. Allow the eggshell to dry. Attach a pipette with tubing to the natural gas outlet. Put the narrow end of the pipette inside one of the holes in the eggshell. Blow natural gas (methane) into the eggshell for 5–10 seconds. Turn off the gas and remove the pipette. Take the shell to an area away from where you filled it. Attach the eggshell to a ringstand. Light the candle at the end of a long stick. Ask students what will happen and what they will observe when you apply the flame to the bottom of the eggshell. Hold the flame an inch or so below the bottom of the eggshell. It should explode in an impressive fireball.

After the demonstrations are completed, ask students to finish the remainder of their worksheets.

Answer the following questions:

1. How well did your sparkler perform? What would you do to improve your sparkler in the future?
2. Why doesn't the sparkler stop burning as soon as the match is removed? Why does the sparkler keep going?

Part II: Explosions – observe the demonstrations, then answer the following:

1. Why didn't the pile of flour burn as well as the flour blown through the surgical tube?
2. Is the popping of a balloon an example of an explosion? Why or why not?
3. Is a sparkler an example of an explosion? Why or why not?
4. In your opinion, which demonstration was the best example of an explosion? What is your reasoning?
5. What did you feel when the methane-filled eggshell went off? What was it that you were actually feeling?
6. Do explosions always involve combustion or fire? Explain.

Making sense:

What conditions appear to be necessary for an explosion to take place?

Part III: Fire Tetrahedron

Some fire scientists have proposed that the fire triangle be replaced by a fire tetrahedron. On the right is a representation of a fire tetrahedron. It is a three dimensional shape with four sides.

According to fire scientists the four sides would be labeled:

- Fuel
- Heat
- Oxygen
- Chemical Chain Reaction

Heat

1. Explain what you think scientists mean by a "chemical chain reaction."
2. Why might the fire tetrahedron be more accurate than the old fire triangle?

Making Sense Discussion (10–15 min)

Major goals: This lesson serves as a summarizing lesson to Investigation II. The conditions that affect the burning of a fire should be fleshed out in this discussion. Several of these concepts should be highlighted. For example, a fire will not continue without an uninhibited chemical chain reaction to sustain it. This leads to the introduction of a fourth condition necessary for fire, and the fire tetrahedron as a replacement for the familiar fire triangle. Also, explosions sometimes (but don't always) accompany combustion, and are the result of a rapid expansion of gases. The surface area of a fuel, and its degree of mixing with oxygen can affect the progress of a fire, or even the presence of an explosion. The fire concept map should be posted and brought up to date at the end of class.

6. Introduce the fire tetrahedron: (Handout – optional)

Have your own 3-dimensional fire tetrahedron on hand to show students at the appropriate time. If you wish you can pass out the Fire Tetrahedron Cutout Sheets to individual students along with scissors and glue sticks. Alternatively, students can take the fire tetrahedron with them to assemble at home.

Discussion goals:

Introduce the concept of a sustained chemical chain reaction as a vital part of every fire.

Sample questions:

Once the sparkler was lit it continued to burn on its own. Why isn't it necessary to keep a match in contact with materials that are combustible?

What do you think a "sustained chemical chain reaction" is?

Points to cover:

Many of those who study the science of fires say it is not always enough to start a fire with fuel, oxygen, and heat. In fact, we can light a piece of paper with a match and it may go out all on its own if we remove the match. Why? Because a fire *is* an uninhibited chemical chain reaction, and if that chemical reaction cannot proceed, the fire will go out.

Consider the sparkler you burned earlier. The heat from the match was transferred to the chemicals stuck on the sparkler, causing them to combust. This combustion reaction released heat. This in turn heated up neighboring chemicals on the sparkler and they combusted. The whole thing is a chain reaction, with heat being transferred from the combustion of a few atoms of the substance to initiate the combustion of neighboring atoms.

Sometimes there is too large a quantity of a fuel to sustain a chemical chain reaction and a fire will go out even though the material is combustible. Other times the fuel cannot get enough oxygen to sustain the chemical reaction. We saw this with the pile of baking flour. Mixing a fuel with oxygen or making sure the fuel is in small pieces are two ways of insuring that a fire can sustain itself.

To account for this aspect of fire, scientists have proposed a fire tetrahedron. (Show students your 3-D model.)

Instructions:
Cut out the figure below. Fold on the dotted lines. Fold and glue the tabs to create a 3-dimensional tetrahedron.

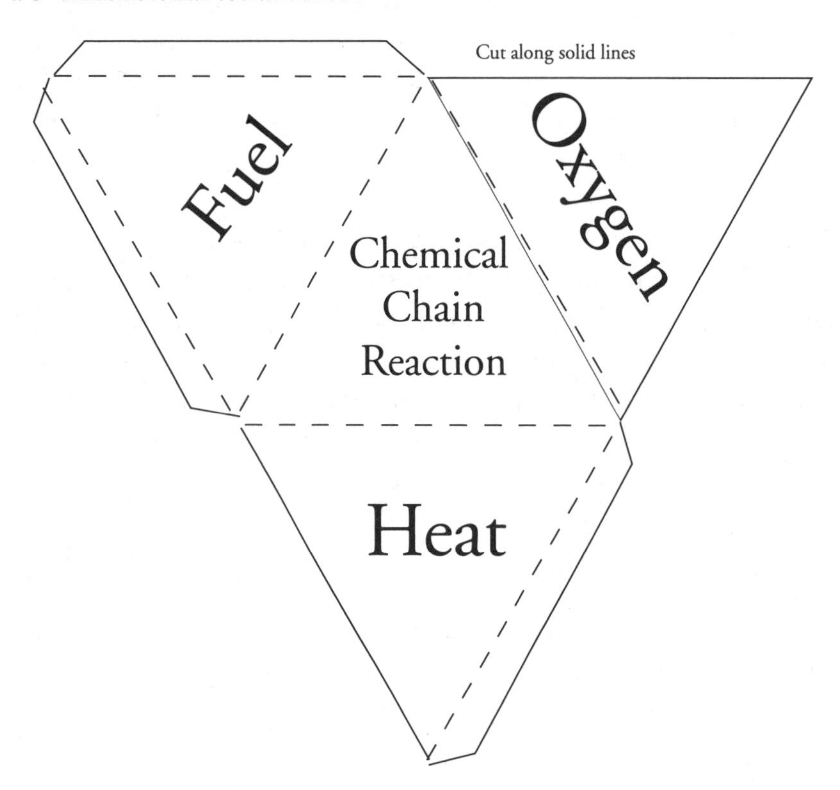

7. Discuss explosions.

Discussion goals:
Assist students in articulating the features of an explosion, and the conditions necessary for an explosion to occur.

Sample questions:

What features does an explosion have?

How can you tell when you've experienced and explosion? (loud noise, shock wave)

Do explosions always have fires? (No)

Do fires always have explosions with them? (No)

How can we predict when combustion will result in an explosion?

When carbon-containing fuels burn, CO_2 (g) and H_2O (g) are formed. Explain why the formation of these gases in a small space can lead to an explosion.

Do you think you can have an explosion if gases are not produced? Why or why not?

Points to cover:
An **explosion** is defined as the effect that occurs when there is a violent expansion of gases. We witnessed several explosions in today's class, some of which involved combustion. The popping of a balloon is an example of an explosion that does not involve combustion. All you really need for an explosion is gas that is expanding quickly. The force of an explosion comes from the gases themselves, moving quickly from an area of high pressure to an area of lower pressure.

When combustion happens extremely rapidly, explosions often result. This is because during combustion, carbon-containing substances are being turned into gases at an extremely fast pace. As you may recall, gases take up much more space than solids or liquids.

The rate that combustion takes place is affected by a number of factors. One factor in the rate of reaction is the accessibility of the fuel to oxygen. Thus, when the fuel and the oxygen are more thoroughly mixed, it is easier for the individual molecules and atoms to interact, and therefore, easier for combustion to take place.

Some work places that deal with very finely divided dry substances, are dangerously prone to explosions. When flour, sawdust, or grain dust are suspended in the air, in a closed space, they become an explosion hazard. Any stray spark or open flame could set this air-fuel mixture off. Flour mills and grain silos go to great lengths to remove any possible sources of sparks, including small stones, which may accidentally cause a spark and set off an explosion.

8. Update Fire Map.

Add information regarding chemical chain reactions and explosions to the Fire Map.

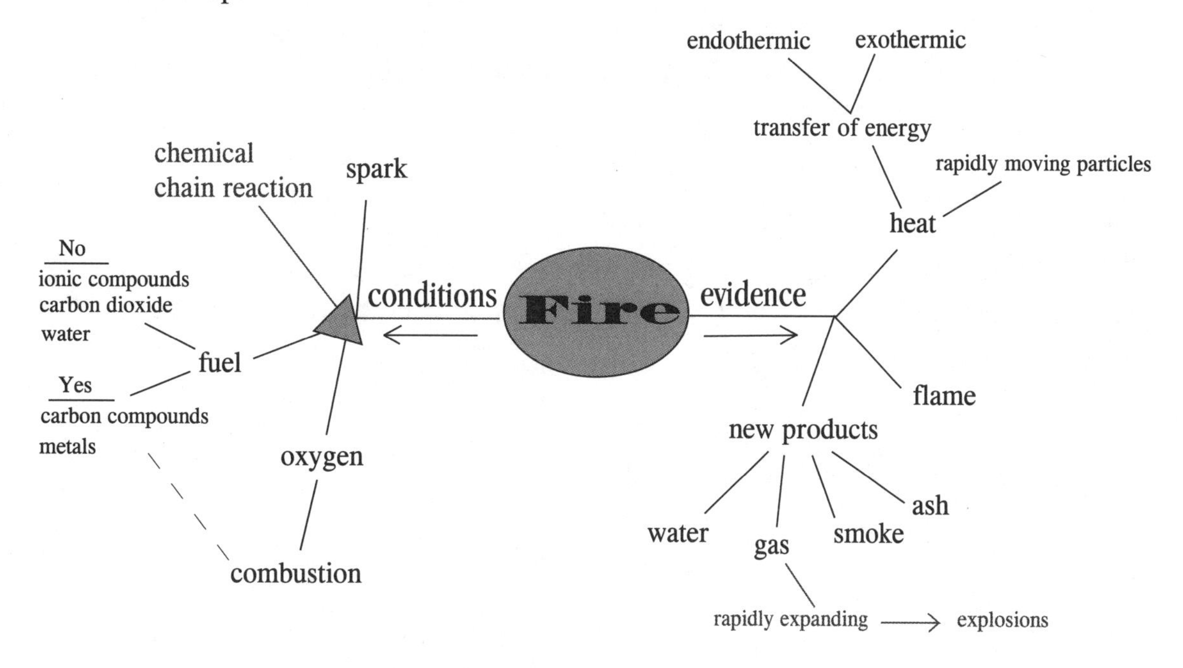

Check-in (5 min)

9. Introduce the Check-in exercise.

Write the following exercise on the board for students to complete individually.

- Explain what is meant by the statement, "Fuels with small molecular masses (such as CH_3OH, methanol) burn better than fuels with large molecular masses (such as C_8H_{14}, octane)." Why do you think this is true?

10. Discuss the Check-in exercise.

Get a sense of the level of understanding by taking a vote, collecting students' work, or asking students to defend their choices.

Discussion goals:
Make sure students have an understanding of the factors that affect the rate of a combustion reaction.

Sample questions:
Which requires more oxygen to burn, CH_3OH or C_8H_{14}?
Why do you think it is more difficult to burn a substance if more oxygen is required per mole?

11. Wrap-up

Assist the students in summarizing what was learned in the class.

- An explosion is a rapid expansion of gases.
- Not all fires involve explosions.
- Some explosions do not involve fire at all.
- The surface area of a fuel, and the availability of oxygen to the fuel, are factors that affect the rate of combustion.
- There are four conditions necessary for fire. These four conditions are represented in the fire tetrahedron: oxygen, fuel, heat (or spark), and chemical chain reaction.

Homework

12. Assign homework.

Use the homework provided with the curriculum or assign your own.

Homework – Investigation II – Lesson 6

1. Find an adult who has heard of the fire triangle. Explain to that adult what the fire tetrahedron is and why it might be more accurate than the fire triangle.
2. Explain how the size of a fuel may have an effect on the lighting and burning of the fuel.
3. It is easier to light a pile of twigs on fire than a large log. It is also easier to burn a pile of twigs than a pile of sawdust. The sawdust is the smallest form of the fuel – why doesn't the sawdust burn easier?
4. Why isn't there an explosion with every fire?
5. When explosions occur in action movies people are often knocked off their feet. What exactly is knocking the people over?
6. What are some ways to prevent explosions during combustion?

Kablooie!

Name: ____________________

Period: ____ Date: ___________

Purpose: In this lesson you will be allowed to test your sparkler. Then you will observe a series of demonstrations related to explosions. Finally, you will be introduced to the Fire Tetrahedron.

Part I: Observe Your Sparkler

SAFETY NOTE: Goggles should be worn by all. The sparklers will emit sparks. You may wish to protect your skin. Those testing the sparklers should not be wearing loose or highly flammable clothing.

Instructions:

1. Hold your sparkler by the end that is bare metal.
2. Point your sparkler away from others and away from combustible materials.
3. Light a match and hold it to the end of your sparkler until it begins to burn.
4. Observe your sparkler until it stops burning. The charred wire may be hot. Dispose of it properly as instructed by your teacher.

Answer the following questions:

1. How well did your sparkler perform? What would you do to improve your sparkler in the future?

2. Why doesn't the sparkler stop burning as soon as the match is removed? Why does the sparkler keep going?

Part II: Explosions – observe the demonstrations, then answer the following:

1. Why didn't the pile of flour burn as well as the flour blown through the surgical tube?

2. Is the popping of a balloon an example of an explosion? Why or why not?

3. Is a sparkler an example of an explosion? Why or why not?

4. In your opinion, which demonstration was the best example of an explosion? What is your reasoning?

5. What did you feel when the methane-oxygen balloon went off? What was it that you were actually feeling?

6. Do explosions always involve combustion or fire? Explain.

Making sense:
What conditions appear to be necessary for an explosion to take place?

Part III: Fire Tetrahedron

Some fire scientists have proposed that the fire triangle be replaced by a fire tetrahedron. On the right is a representation of a fire tetrahedron. It is a three dimensional shape with four sides.

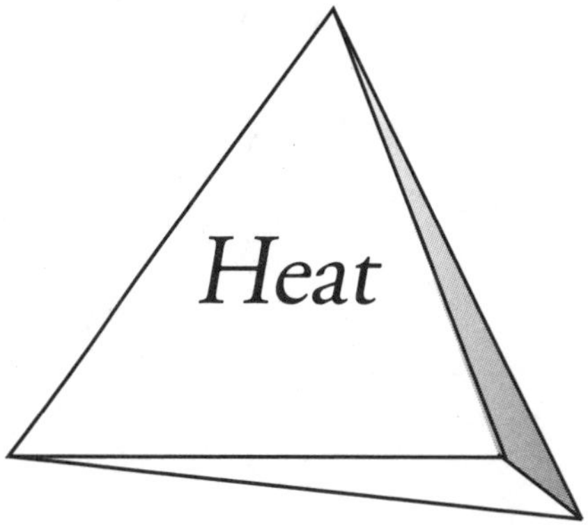

According to fire scientists the four sides would be labeled:
1. Fuel
2. Heat
3. Oxygen
4. Chemical Chain Reaction

Heat

1. Explain what you think fire scientists mean by a chemical chain reaction.

2. Why might a fire tetrahedron be more accurate than the old fire triangle?

Create a Fire Tetrahedron: (optional)

Cut out the figure below. Fold on the dotted lines. Fold and glue the tabs to create a 3-dimensional tetrahedron.

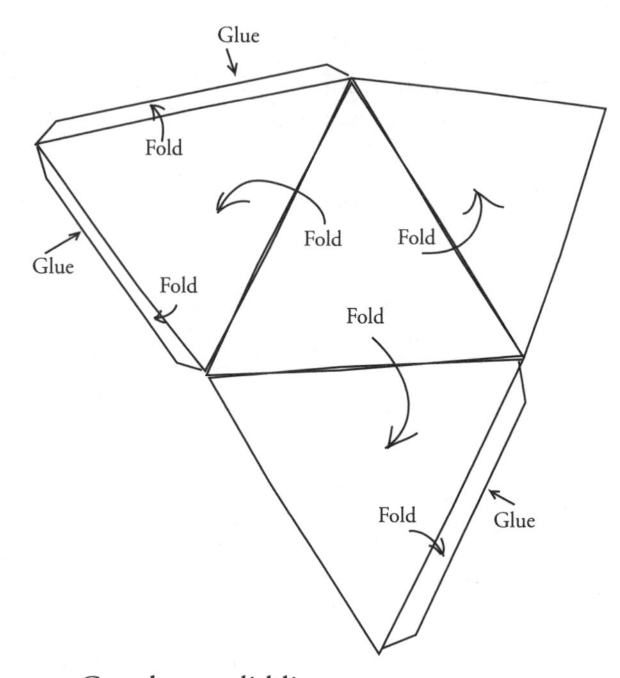

Cut along solid lines

Fuel

Oxygen

Chemical
Chain
Reaction

Heat

Unit 5: Fire

Investigation III: Energy for Change

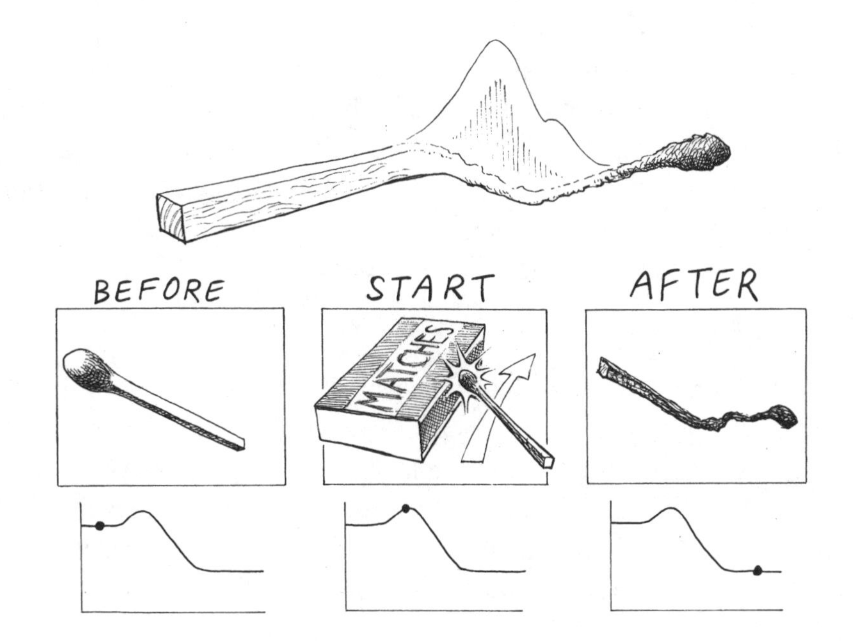

Contents of Investigation II *Page*

Investigation III Summary:

Energy for Change

Lesson 1 – No Going Back This lesson opens up the third investigation, which is devoted to examining and explaining fire, combustion, and chemical change in general, on a particulate level. Change is always accompanied by energy exchanges. Tracking the energy into and out of a system can help us to interpret what is going on at a particulate level. In this first lesson, students use energy diagrams to track energy changes as a reaction proceeds from reactants to products. Heats of reaction and the law of conservation of energy are introduced.

Lesson 2 – Fire Starter In this lesson, students learn that bond making is exothermic while bond breaking is endothermic. Both events happen in every chemical reaction. The first step of any chemical reaction is the breaking of "old" bonds. This step requires an input of energy called the activation energy. If other circumstances are the same, reactions with high energies of activation are less likely to occur than those with low energies of activation. Once a reaction has been initiated, "new" bonds form with release of energy.

Lesson 3 – Formations This lesson introduces the tables of heats of formation, which can be used to determine the heat of a reaction. The term enthalpy is introduced in this lesson, as being more accurate than the term heat of reaction. Enthalpy takes into account changes in pressure due to the presence of gases in either the reactants or the products. The enthalpy of a reaction can be calculated if the enthalpies of the reactants and products are known: $\Delta H_{rxn} = \Delta H(\text{products}) - \Delta H(\text{reactants})$.

Lesson 4 – Ashes to Ashes This lesson wraps up the Fire Unit. It provides students with practice applying the concepts they have learned throughout these investigations. Students complete a worksheet that covers the material that was presented during the unit. In addition, the Fire Concept Map helps to organize and summarize the remaining concepts that were introduced.

BEFORE CLASS...

LESSON 1 – No Going Back

Key Ideas:
The energy of the reactants and products of a reaction are not the same. The energy differs by the heat of the reaction. For exothermic processes, the energy of the products is lower and the heat of reaction is negative. For endothermic processes, the energy of the products is higher and the heat of the reaction is positive. Energy is conserved in chemical processes. This means that the energy required to reverse a process is equal and opposite to the energy required to cause the forward process.

Students have experience with many reversible reactions (e.g., in the copper cycle experiment in Alchemy). This lesson focuses on irreversible reactions (e.g., the coal combustion), and what makes them irreversible.

What Takes Place:
Students observe two demonstrations by the instructor – one showing the formation of water by oxidation of hydrogen, the other showing the formation of hydrogen and oxygen from water. Students are then introduced to rudimentary energy diagrams. They consider how to use these diagrams to discuss the energies of the reactants and products in the combustion of fuels such as hydrogen and methane. Students are introduced to the law of conservation of energy. The lesson ends with a discussion of the implications of conservation of energy for the burning of fossil fuels.

Set Up Hydrogen Balloon
Before class prepare a balloon filled with hydrogen by reacting magnesium in hydrochloric acid. Place about 100 mL of 1 M HCl in a 250-mL Erlenmeyer flask. Put magnesium pieces (~1.0 g) inside a balloon. Put the balloon over the mouth of the flask without allowing the magnesium to fall into the HCl. Once the balloon is securely sealed on the flask, shake the deflated balloon to allow the magnesium to drop into the flask. The reaction between the magnesium and HCl generates H_2 gas, which inflates the balloon to about 1 liter. Once the reaction is complete, tie off the balloon. Since the balloon is less dense than air, be sure to tie a string onto the balloon so that you do not lose it. Hydrogen balloons can be made the morning before their use. They don't "save" well overnight.

Set Up Water Electrolysis
Put about 800 mL of water in a 1000-mL beaker. Add about 15 teaspoons salt. Stir until all the salt dissolves. Fold two 8 cm x 8 cm pieces of aluminum foil so that you have two flat strips about 8 cm x 1 cm. Hang the two strips from the side of the beaker. Do not allow the two strips to touch one another.

Materials:

- Student worksheet
- 100 mL 1 M HCl
- 1 g magnesium
- 1 250-mL Erlenmeyer flask
- 1 balloon (to fill with H_2 generated by the reaction of Mg and HCl)
- 1 ring stand with a ring
- 1 foot of string (for the H_2 balloon)
- 1 dowel with taper candle attached
- matches
- 1 1000-mL beaker
- 800 mL salt water
- 15 teaspoons salt
- 2 pieces of aluminum foil (about 8 cm x 8 cm)
- 1 9-volt battery
- 2 wires with alligator clips (to attach the battery to the aluminum foil)
- 2 test tubes (optional: to collect the gases produced)

Investigation III – Energy for Change

LESSON 1 – No Going Back

This lesson opens up the third investigation, which is devoted to examining and explaining fire, combustion, and chemical change in general, on a particulate level. Change is always accompanied by energy exchanges. Tracking the energy into and out of a system can help us to interpret what is going on at a particulate level. In this first lesson, students use energy diagrams to track energy changes as a reaction proceeds from reactants to products. Heats of reaction and the law of conservation of energy are introduced.

Exploring the Topic (10 min)

1. Introduce the ChemCatalyst exercise.

Write the following exercise on the board for students to complete individually.

Humans generate energy from burning fuels, such as coal, oil, natural gas, and hydrogen. For example, the combustion of coal can be written as

$$C\ (s) + O_2\ (g) \rightarrow CO_2\ (g)$$

- Do you think you can reverse the reaction to form coal, C(s), and oxygen, O_2, from CO_2? Explain your thinking.

2. Discuss the ChemCatalyst exercise.

Use the discussion to get a sense of students' initial ideas.

Discussion goals:

Use the students' written responses to stimulate a discussion about what is required to reverse a combustion reaction.

Sample questions:

Is heat absorbed or released when coal burns?

If heat is released in a reaction, does the energy of the system go up or down?

Is the energy of the CO_2 higher or lower than the energy of the C and O_2?

Write the reverse reaction. Describe what you would observe if the reverse reaction occurred.

There is gaseous CO_2 in the atmosphere. Have you ever observed the CO_2 react to form solid carbon and oxygen? (Does charcoal rain fall from the skies?)

Do you think the reverse reaction actually occurs? Explain your thinking.

Give students a chance to think about the connection between heat and the energies of the reactants and the products. Let them discuss how they think heat is associated with the direction of a reaction. Students are likely to say that they have not observed carbon rain (!) so it seems that reversing the combustion of coal is difficult. Some may realize that since heat is released when coal combusts, heat is required to reverse the reaction. Be sure to let them express their ideas about energy. Some will realize that since heat is released, the energy of the system decreases as the products form. At this point in the lesson, accept all answers without judgment.

3. Complete the demonstrations.

You will do two demonstrations, one to show the combustion of water and the second to show the reverse reaction, the decomposition of water.

SAFETY NOTE: Wear safety glasses while performing these demonstrations. Keep hair and loose clothing away from flames. Make sure students are at least 10 feet away from the demonstration table. Be sure to have a fire extinguisher available.

DEMO 1 – Hydrogen Balloon

Materials:

1 small balloon filled with hydrogen (fill before class by reaction of Mg + HCl)
1 ring stand with a ring
1 foot of string (for the H_2 balloon)
1 dowel with taper candle attached
1 lit candle
matches

Tell students that you will be reacting hydrogen with oxygen. A small spark is needed to initiate the reaction. Tie the H_2 balloon on the ring of the ring stand. Do not have a lot of extra string because it can catch on fire when the balloon ignites. Light the taper candle on the dowel. Tell students to plug their ears. You should put earplugs or cotton balls in your ears. Hold the candle under the balloon until the balloon explodes.

Suggested questions:

What evidence do you have that this was combustion, and not just the balloon popping?

What evidence did you have that the combustion of hydrogen was an exothermic reaction?

Once you get a fuel to start burning, do you need to do anything to keep it burning?

DEMO 2 – Decomposition Water:

Materials:

1 1000-mL beaker
800 mL salt water (about 1 teaspoon per 50 mL)
9 volt battery
2 wires with alligator clips (to attach the battery to the aluminum foil)
2 pieces of aluminum foil (about 8 x 8 cm accordion folded into a flat strip)
2 test tubes (optional: to collect the gases produced)

Tell students that you will be using electrical energy to split apart molecules of water, H_2O, into molecules of hydrogen, H_2, and oxygen, O_2. Take the beaker with salt water that you have prepared before class. Hang the two strips of aluminum foil on the beaker so that a sufficient length of aluminum is in the salt solution. The two strips should not be touching one another. Attach the battery with the alligator clips, one side to each strip of aluminum. You will see bubbles forming around both pieces of aluminum after about a minute or so. One set of bubbles is hydrogen, the other oxygen. Unplug the battery to show that bubbles only appear when energy is supplied (in this case in the form of electrical energy).

If you wish, you can collect the gases. Submerge a test tube in the beaker so that it is completely filled with water. Turn the tube upside down with the closed end above the water so that you can clamp it. Position the open end near one of the electrodes to capture the bubbles. Slowly, the gases will collect in the test tubes (you will see the water level inside the test tubes decrease. The gas volume will be in the ratio of 2:1, 2 moles of H_2 for every 1 mole of O_2.

Suggested questions:

Was the decomposition of water exothermic or endothermic? Explain your thinking.

If you unplug the battery, do you still observe hydrogen and oxygen bubbles forming?

4. Introduce energy diagrams. (Transparency)

Display the transparency on an overhead projector.

Points to cover:

We can illustrate the energy in and out of these two reactions in diagrams. The first diagram represents the combustion reaction for hydrogen. The second diagram represents the decomposition of water reaction.

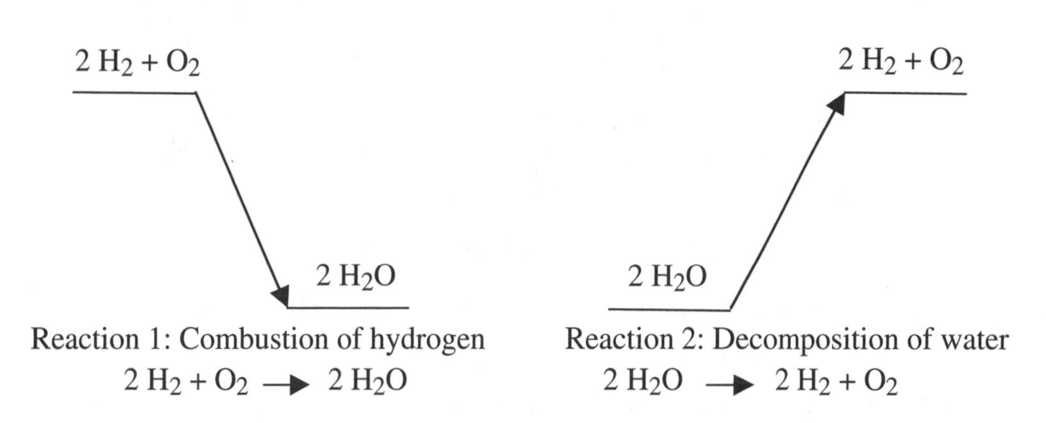

Reaction 1: Combustion of hydrogen

$2\ H_2 + O_2 \rightarrow 2\ H_2O$

Reaction 2: Decomposition of water

$2\ H_2O \rightarrow 2\ H_2 + O_2$

The diagrams you see on the transparency are referred to as **energy diagrams.** They show the difference in energy from the beginning of a reaction to the end of the reaction. Or, you could also say they show the difference in energy between the reactants and the products. Today's lesson will help you to understand and interpret these diagrams.

5. Explain the purpose of today's activity.

If you wish you can write the main question on the board.

Points to cover:

Tell students they will examine the energy changes from the beginning of a reaction to the end. As they think about the energies of the reactants and the products, they will answer the question: "How can you reverse a combustion reaction?"

Activity – No Going Back (15 min)

6. Introduce the activity. (Worksheet)

Pass out the worksheets. Ask students to work in pairs.

Answer the following questions:

Refer to the diagrams below to answer Questions 1–3.

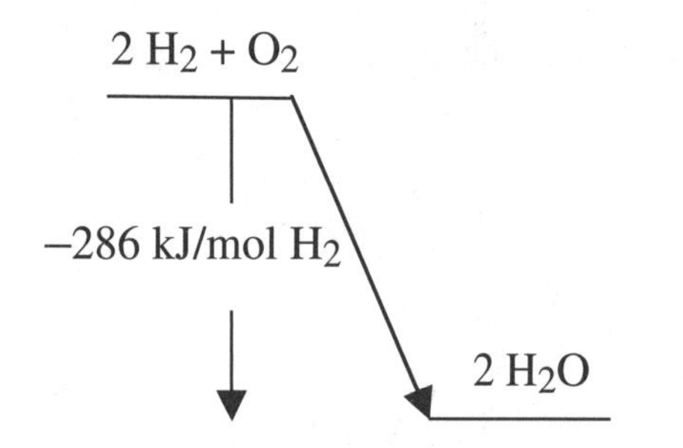

Reaction 1: Combustion of hydrogen

$2\,H_2 + O_2 \rightarrow 2\,H_2O$

$2\,H_2 + O_2$

$+286$ kJ/mol H_2

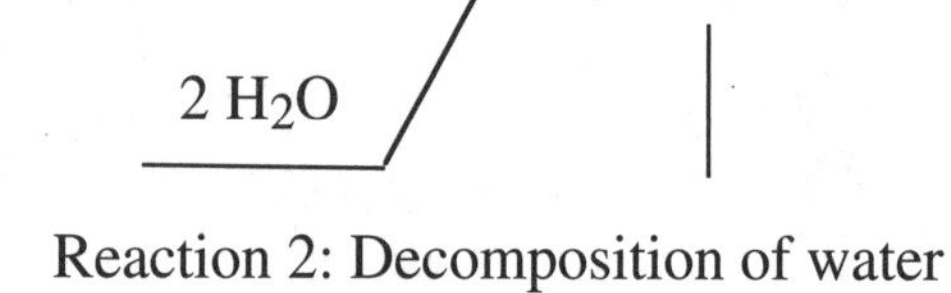

Reaction 2: Decomposition of water

$2\,H_2O \rightarrow 2\,H_2 + O_2$

1. Consider the combustion of hydrogen.
   a. Is energy required or released for the combustion of hydrogen? Use evidence from the demonstration to explain your thinking. (Released – after you get the fire started, it continues on its own.)
   b. Will the reaction feel hot or cold? (hot)
   c. Does the energy increase or decrease in going from reactants to products? (decreases)
2. Consider the decomposition of water.
   a. How is the decomposition of water related to the combustion of hydrogen? (They are the reverse of one another.)

b. Is energy required or released for the decomposition of water? Explain your thinking. (Required – you need to put in energy to produce hydrogen and oxygen from water.)

c. Does the reaction feel hot or cold? (cold)

d. Does the energy increase or decrease in going from reactants to products? (increases)

3. The number in kJ/mol H_2 given on both diagrams is called the **heat of reaction.**

   a. Explain why one of the two heats of reaction has a positive sign and the other has a negative sign. (When the sign is negative, heat is released. When the sign is positive, heat is absorbed.)

   b. **Energy is conserved** whenever you reverse a reaction. Use the diagrams to explain what this means.

Fill in the boxes in the diagram below and then answer Questions 4–7:

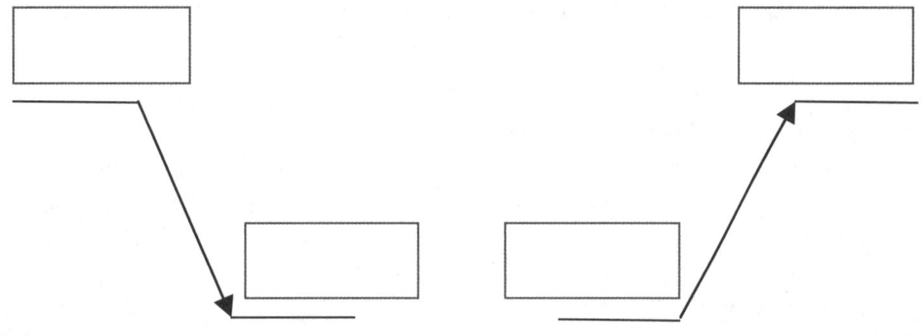

Reaction 1: Combustion of methane
$CH_4 + 2\ O_2 \rightarrow CO_2 + 2\ H_2O$

Reaction 2: Formation of methane
$CO_2 + 2\ H_2O \rightarrow CH_4 + 2\ O_2$

4. The heat of reaction for the combustion of methane is –891 kJ/mol CH_4. What is the heat of reaction for the formation of methane from carbon dioxide and water? (+891 kJ/mol H_2)

5. Can you tell if a reaction is exothermic or endothermic just by looking at its energy diagram? Explain. (For an exothermic reaction, the energy of the products is lower than the energy of the reactants. The opposite is true for an endothermic reaction.)

6. If you use natural gas in your home, then you are using the combustion of methane to transfer heat. List two ways in which you use the heat of the combustion reaction. (Heating the air to keep the room temperature comfortable, heating water for showers, and for washing dishes and clothing, and cooking)

7. The combustion of methane produces carbon dioxide and water. If you put carbon dioxide and water together, do you expect to form methane? Why or why not?

Making sense:
Humans generate energy from burning fuels we dig out of the earth, such as coal, oil, and natural gas. Do you think it will be easy to replenish these fuels? Explain your thinking.

If you finish early...
Is every reaction on the planet reversible? Explain your reasoning. Think about energy diagrams in completing your answer.

Making Sense Discussion (15 min)

Major goals: The main focus of this discussion is on comparing the energies of the reactants with the energies of the products for exothermic and endothermic reactions. Students discuss the significance of releasing a lot of energy in the form of heat in a combustion reaction. When heat is released, the energy of the system is lowered. This means that a very large input of energy is required to reverse the reaction to reform the fuel.

7. Discuss the energy diagrams.

You may wish to draw sample energy diagrams on the board for students to discuss. Alternatively, you can have students come to the board to draw and label their own diagrams.

Discussion goals:
Provide students with the opportunity to discuss the energies of the reactants and products.

Sample questions:
What does the energy diagram tell you?
Sketch an example of a diagram for an exothermic reaction.
Sketch an example of a diagram for a very weakly endothermic reaction.
What does it mean that the products are lower in energy compared with the reactants?
What is the heat of the reaction?
How are heat and energy related in these diagrams?

Points to cover:
An energy diagram shows the difference between the energies of the reactants and the products of a chemical process. The difference in energy is called the **heat of the reaction.** The heat of the reaction is the heat that we measure in a calorimetry experiment such as the burning Cheeto® experiment.

Notice that we have not really defined the vertical axis of the energy diagram. In other words, we have not really provided a precise definition of what kind of energy we are talking about. This is because the concept of energy is quite complex and difficult to pin down. When we say the energy of the products is lower than the energy of the reactants, for a specific chemical reaction, we mean that the products form through the release of energy in the form of heat. Likewise, the reactants form only with energy input. We can measure the difference in energy between reactants and products by tracking the heat. However, we do not have a good way of directly measuring the energy content of the reactants or the energy content of the products. As you will see, even if our definition of energy is not very precise, it is very useful to use heat transfer and calorimetry to analyze changes in energy.

Heat of reaction is the amount of energy gained or lost during a chemical reaction. If the sign for the heat of reaction is negative, the reaction is exothermic. If the sign is positive, the reaction is endothermic.

8. Introduce the law of conservation of energy.

Discussion goals:

Provide students with the opportunity to discuss the implications of the law of conservation of energy.

Sample questions:

What does it mean that energy is conserved?

Is it possible to get more energy out of the combustion of a fuel than is required to form the fuel by the reverse reaction? Why or why not?

What does it mean that energy is conserved when you reverse a reaction?

Points to cover:

Through many observations, scientists have concluded that energy is neither created nor destroyed. This is known as the **law of conservation of energy.** No one has ever proven conservation of energy. However, no one has ever observed an example of a process that does not conserve energy.

The law of conservation of energy is useful in analyzing the energies of the forward and reverse directions of chemical reactions. If we know the heat of reaction for a certain process, then we know that the reverse reaction will occur with an equal amount of energy transferred in the opposite direction.

Conservation of energy is a law that states that energy is neither created nor destroyed. Thus, if a chemical process releases energy, then the reverse process must require an input of the exact same amount of energy.

9. Discuss replenishment of fuels that we burn.

Discussion goals:
Provide students with the opportunity to discuss replenishment of fuels.

Sample questions:
What is the reverse reaction of the combustion of methane?
How do you think it is possible to form methane?
What role do you think sunlight might have in the formation of fuels?
Given what you understand about energy exchanges, should humans worry about burning so much of the fuels stored in the earth? Why or why not?

Points to cover:
Humans generate energy for various needs by burning wood, or by burning fuels we dig out of the earth, such as coal, oil, and natural gas. These are precious resources that have come into the existence after decades of growing (as in the case of trees) or millions of years of decay of matter derived from living things (as in the case of the so-called fossil fuels). For example, we burn natural gas (methane) in our homes to heat the air to keep the temperature in our homes comfortable, to heat water for showers and for washing dishes and clothing, and to cook food on our stoves. Each of us burns massive amounts of these fuels each day. What took many years to make is rapidly converted to carbon dioxide and water.

The reverse reaction requires energy. While combustion reactions require a spark for initiation, the reaction continues on its own once initiated. This is not true of the reverse reaction. A constant supply of energy is required to drive the reaction in the reverse direction.

The main source of energy for creating fuels is the sun. Sunlight causes plants to produce fuels from carbon dioxide and water. Unfortunately, this process is slower than the rate at which we are consuming the stores of fuels. This is clearly an important frontier of science: how to harness energy from the sun more efficiently than by burning fuels created over millions of years.

Check-in (5 min)

10. Introduce the Check-in exercise.

Write the following exercise on the board for students to complete individually.

- Sketch an energy diagram for the combustion of carbon (coal) to form carbon dioxide. The heat of reaction is –394 kJ/mol.
- What energy is required to form coal from carbon dioxide?

11. Discuss the Check-in exercise.

Get a sense of the level of understanding by taking a vote, collecting students' work, or asking students to defend their choices.

Discussion goals:

Make sure students understand how to use an energy diagram to examine the energies of the reactants and products of a reaction.

Sample questions:

What are the reactants in the combustion of coal?
What are the products?
Are the reactants higher or lower in energy compared with the products?
What does it mean that the heat of reaction for the combustion of carbon is negative?
What energy is required to reverse the reaction?

12. Wrap-up

Assist the students in summarizing what was learned in the class.

- The heat of reaction is the energy change in going from reactants to products.
- The heat of reaction is positive for an endothermic reaction. It is negative for an exothermic reaction.
- Energy is conserved in a chemical reaction. The reverse reaction requires an equal amount of energy transferred in the opposite direction.

Homework

13. Assign homework.

Use the homework provided with the curriculum or assign your own.

Homework – Investigation III – Lesson 1

1. When methane combusts with oxygen, 891 kJ/mol of energy are exchanged between the system and the surroundings. Draw the energy diagram for this reaction.
2. Draw the energy diagram for the reverse reaction.
3. What are the values of the heat of reaction for each reaction?
4. Which reaction is endothermic and which is exothermic?

Energy Diagrams

Transparency

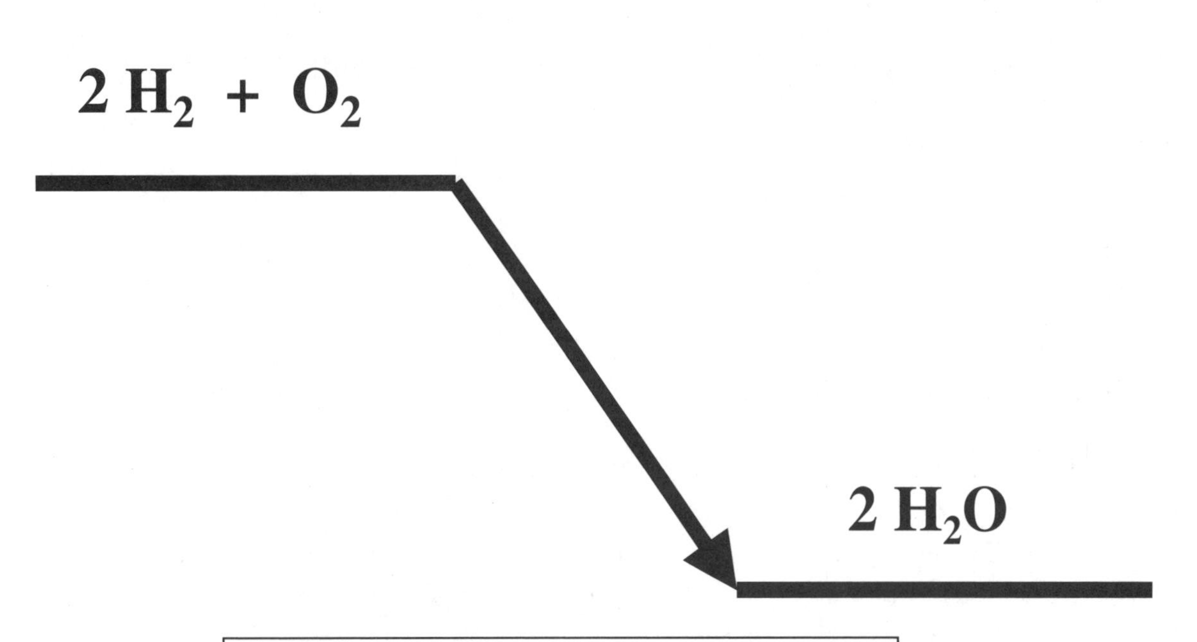

combustion of hydrogen

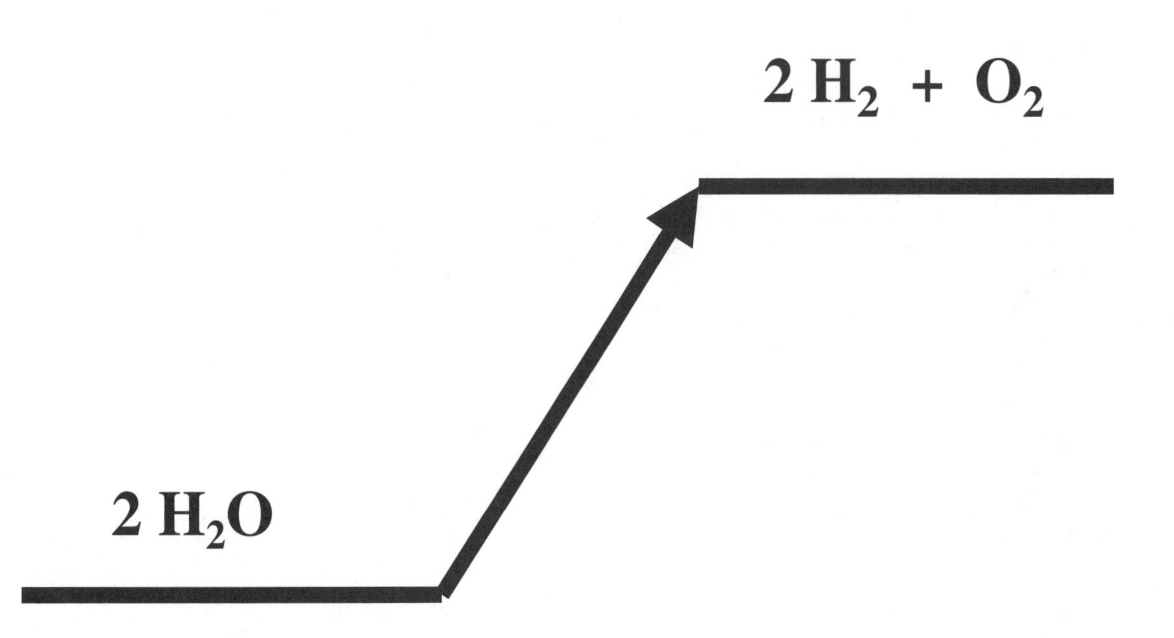

decomposition of water

No Going Back

Name: ______________________

Period: _____ Date: ___________

Purpose: In this lesson you will use energy diagrams to examine the energies from the beginning of a reaction to the end.

Answer the following questions:

Refer to the diagrams below to answer Questions 1–3.

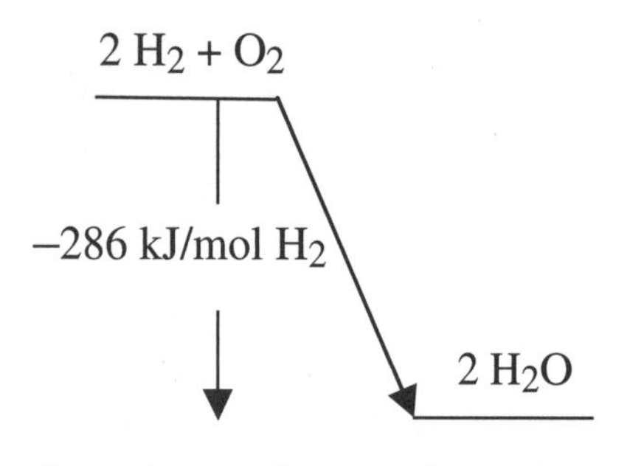

Reaction 1: Combustion of hydrogen
$2\ H_2 + O_2 \rightarrow 2\ H_2O$

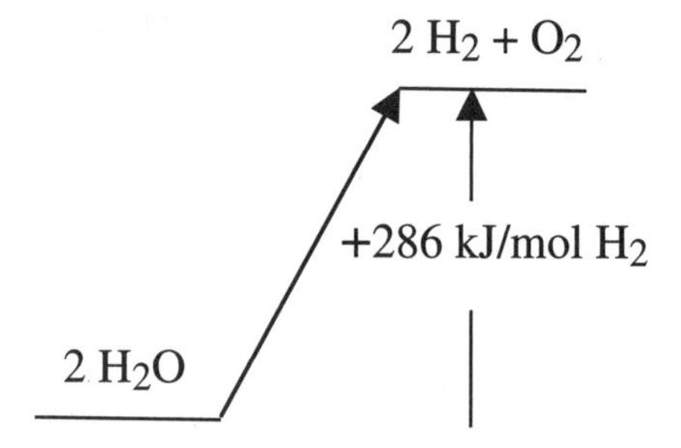

Reaction 2: Decomposition of water
$2\ H_2O \rightarrow 2\ H_2 + O_2$

1. Consider the combustion of hydrogen.
   a. Is energy required or released for the combustion of hydrogen? Use evidence from the demonstration to explain your thinking.
   b. Does the reaction feel hot or cold?
   c. Does the energy increase or decrease in going from reactants to products?
2. Consider the decomposition of water.
   a. How is the decomposition of water related to the combustion of hydrogen?
   b. Is energy required or released for the decomposition of water? Explain your thinking.
   c. Will the reaction feel hot or cold?
   d. Does the energy increase or decrease in going from reactants to products?
3. The number in kJ/mol H_2 given on both diagrams are called the **heat of reaction.**
   a. Explain why one of the two heats of reaction has a positive sign and the other has a negative sign.
   b. **Energy is conserved** whenever you reverse a reaction. Use the diagrams to explain what this means.

Fill in the boxes in the diagram below and then answer Questions 4–7:

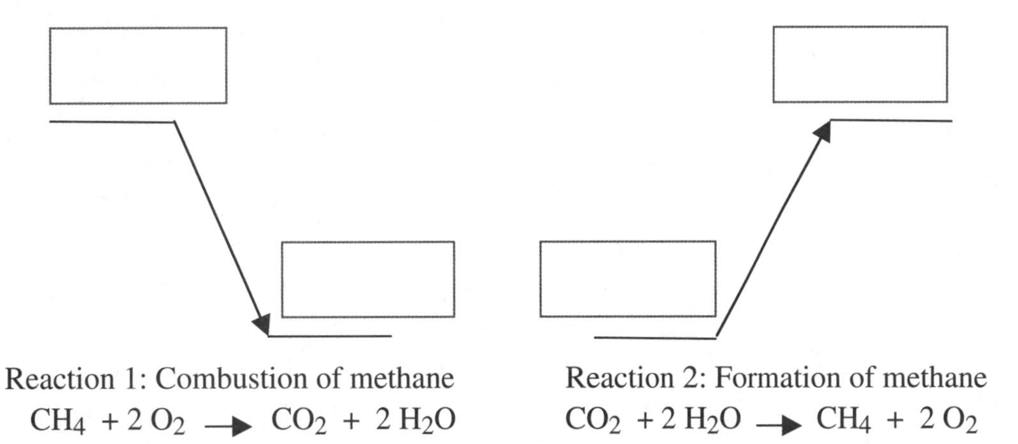

Reaction 1: Combustion of methane
$CH_4 + 2\ O_2 \rightarrow CO_2 + 2\ H_2O$

Reaction 2: Formation of methane
$CO_2 + 2\ H_2O \rightarrow CH_4 + 2\ O_2$

4. The heat of reaction for the combustion of methane is –891 kJ/mol CH_4. What is the heat of reaction for the formation of methane from carbon dioxide and water?

5. Can you tell if a reaction is exothermic or endothermic just by looking at its energy diagram? Explain.

6. If you use natural gas in your home, then you are using the combustion of methane to transfer heat. List two ways in which you use the heat of the combustion reaction.

7. The combustion of methane produces carbon dioxide and water. If you put carbon dioxide and water together, do you expect to form methane? Why or why not?

Making sense:
Humans generate energy from burning fuels we dig out of the earth, such as coal, oil, and natural gas. Do you think it will be easy to replenish these fuels? Explain your thinking.

If you finish early...
Is every reaction on the planet reversible? Explain your reasoning. Think about energy diagrams in completing your answer.

BEFORE CLASS...

LESSON 2 – Fire Starter

Key Ideas:
Breaking bonds is the first step in any chemical rearrangement. It takes energy to break bonds. The initial energy must come from outside the system. Thus, every chemical reaction requires some sort of energy input to get it started. This is called the activation energy. Some reactions have high activation energies, making them more difficult to initiate than reactions with low activation energies. Bond making occurs as part of a chemical rearrangement. Bond making releases energy. Equal and opposite processes have equal and opposite energy transfer. Thus, it takes the same amount of energy to make a bond that it took to break that same bond.

What Takes Place:
Students are briefly introduced to the notion of energy of activation and how it is represented on an energy diagram. They observe a demonstration called "Writing with Fire" that illustrates the lowering of the activation energy for combustion of paper. Then the class is presented with a worksheet that provides them with practice interpreting energy diagrams and relating them to what would be observed macroscopically. The energy of activation and the heat of reaction are related to the energy required for bond breaking and the energy released for bond making.

Set-up
The day before class, prepare a sign that says "Fire" in invisible ink for the demonstration. In a small beaker, add potassium nitrate (about 6 g) to 20 mL of water until you have created a saturated solution. Use a glass stirring rod or a cotton swab to write the word "Fire" on the paper. Make sure that you use cursive or continuous writing so that the letters are all connected to each other. Use plenty of solution and make the lines thick. Put a small mark on the paper where the word begins, for later reference. Let the paper dry at room temperature.

Materials (per class):
- Student worksheet
- 1 50-mL beaker
- 20 mL water
- ~6 g KNO_3, potassium nitrate
- 1 cotton swab or stirring rod
- 1 piece of uncoated paper approximately 8 1/2 x 11"
- matches
- masking tape
- 2 magnets

Investigation III – Energy for Change

LESSON 2 – Fire Starter

In this lesson, students learn that bond making is exothermic while bond breaking is endothermic. Both events happen in every chemical reaction. The first step of any chemical reaction is the breaking of "old" bonds. This step requires an input of energy called the activation energy. If other circumstances are the same, reactions with high energies of activation are less likely to occur than those with low energies of activation. Once a reaction has been initiated, "new" bonds form with release of energy.

Exploring the Topic (10 min)

1. Introduce the ChemCatalyst.

Write the ChemCatalyst exercise on the board for students to complete individually.

In the previous lesson we showed you an energy diagram for the combustion of hydrogen. In actuality, that diagram was simplified. This new energy diagram is more accurate.

- What is different about this diagram? Explain what you think is going on, and why you think the diagram has the shape it has.

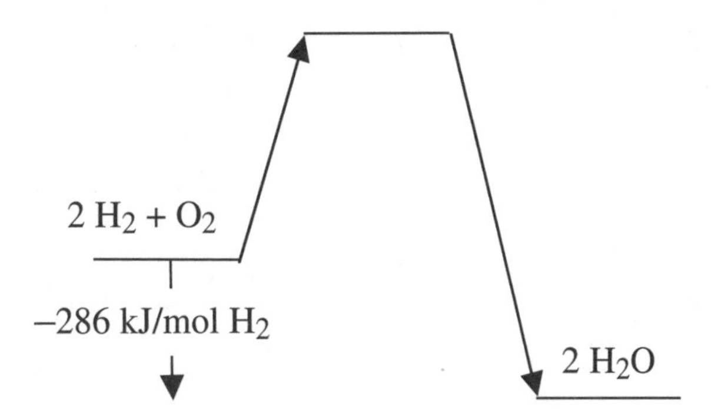

2. Discuss the ChemCatalyst exercise.

Use the discussion to get a sense of students' initial ideas.

<u>Discussion goals:</u>
Use the students' written responses to stimulate a discussion about this new energy diagram.

Sample questions:
Why do you think there is a hill in this energy diagram? What do you think it represents?
What do you think the energy diagram for the reverse reaction would look like?
Is this reaction exothermic or endothermic? Explain.

3. Briefly introduce energy of activation.

Draw the diagram below on the board. Show students that energy diagrams can also be represented as smooth curves (not shown).

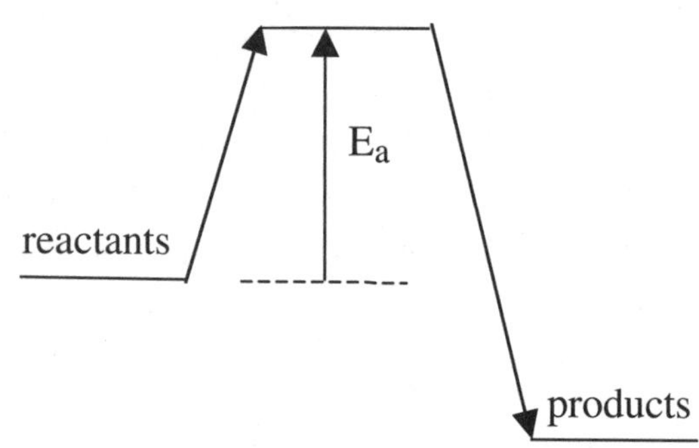

Points to cover:
The hill on the energy diagram represents the energy that it takes to get a reaction started. This energy is called the **energy of activation** or the **activation energy.**

Energy of activation: The energy that is required to get a reaction started.

4. Complete the "Writing with Fire" demonstration.

Demonstration – Writing with Fire
The day before class, prepare the invisible ink sign as directed on the Before Class page. It is suggested that you write the word "Fire" on the paper, but any word will do, as long as the letters are continuous. On the day of the demonstration, show the students the blank paper. Tape it to the board where all can see it. Tell the students you are going to write with fire. Light a match. Make sure it is burning well before blowing it out. Then touch the beginning of your word with the glowing tip of the match. The word will ignite and a glowing front will travel along the path of the dried potassium nitrate solution, leaving behind a black trail of ash. The paper around the word will not burn.

Discussion goals:
Allow students to speculate about what is going on in the "Writing with Fire" demonstration.

Sample questions:
What evidence do you have that combustion took place in the demonstration?
Was the reaction exothermic or endothermic? How do you know?
What usually happens when paper burns?
How was the reaction started?
Why do you think only some of the paper burned?
Why do you think the reaction proceeded without a flame?

Give students a little time to give their observations and discuss what they think might be going on. Tell them that you will get back to discussing the demonstration on the worksheet.

5. Explain the purpose of today's activity.

If you wish you can write the main question on the board.

Points to cover:
Tell students they will be gathering information to explain the demonstration and consider the role of the energy of activation on a reaction. The focus is to answer the question: "What does the activation energy tell us about a reaction?"

Activity – Fire Starter (10–5 min)

6. Introduce the activity. (Worksheet)

Pass out worksheets. Ask students to work individually.

Answer the following questions.

1. The diagrams below show the changes in energy for two different reactions.

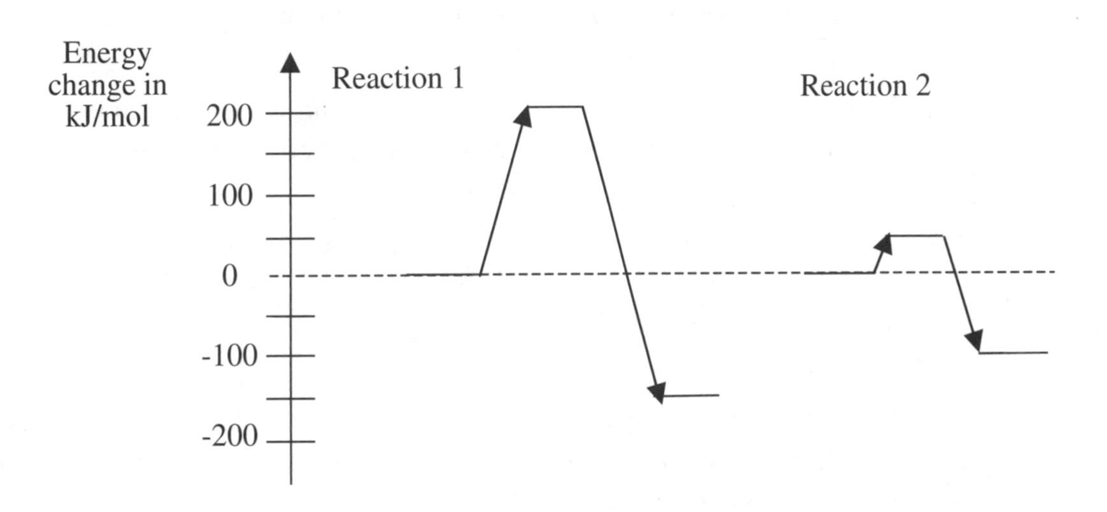

   a. What is the energy of activation for Reaction 1? (200 kJ/mol)
   b. What is the energy of activation for Reaction 2? (50 kJ/mol)
   c. Which reaction requires more energy to get it started? (Reaction 1)
   d. What is the heat of reaction for Reaction 1? (–150 kJ/mol)
   e. What is the heat of reaction for Reaction 2? (–100 kJ/mol)
   a. Which reaction releases more heat? (Reaction 1)

2. The diagram below shows one way to think about a chemical reaction. You can think of the top of the hill as the **transition state,** an intermediate step in the reaction. Some bonds of the reactants are broken to reach the transition state. Then, atoms come together to form the bonds in the products.

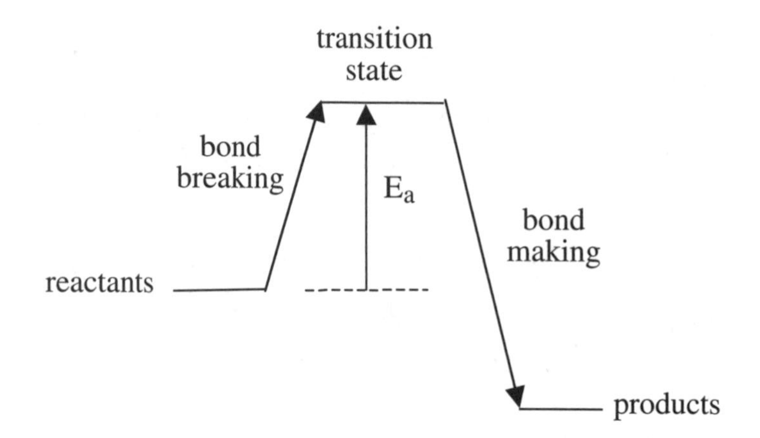

a. Bond breaking requires energy. How is bond breaking related to the energy of activation? Explain your thinking. (You need to break bonds to get a reaction started.)

b. Use the law of conservation of energy to explain why bond making releases energy. (If you need energy to break a bond, the same amount of energy will be released when the same bond forms.)

c. The energy diagram shown represents a combustion reaction. Why is a spark required to get the reaction started? (to supply the energy of activation to break bonds)

d. Heat must be supplied to reverse the reaction because the reverse reaction is endothermic. Do you also need more heat to get the reverse reaction started? Explain. (Yes – more energy is required to break the bonds of the product to get to the transition state.)

3. The two energy diagrams below show the formation of HCl and HBr.

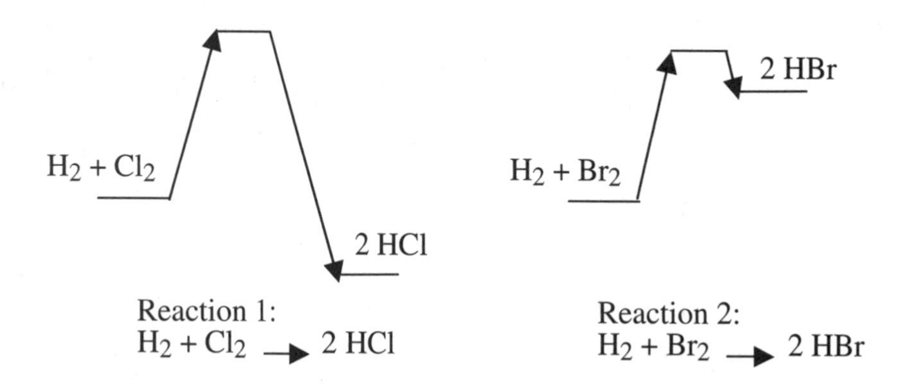

a. Is Reaction 1 exothermic or endothermic? (exothermic)

b. Is Reaction 2 exothermic or endothermic? (endothermic)

c. Which bonds need to be broken to get the reaction started? (H-H, Cl-Cl, and Br-Br)

d. Which bonds need to be formed? (H-Cl and H-Br)

e. For which reaction is the energy required for bond breaking greater than the energy released for bond making? (Reaction 2)

4. In the "Writing with Fire" demonstration, the writing was done with the reaction between potassium nitrate (KNO_3) and paper. Use the diagrams below to explain why the paper ignited with KNO_3. (The energy of activation is lower for the reaction with KNO_3, so it gets started with a match that has been blown out. Without KNO_3, a lit match is needed to start the reaction between paper and oxygen.)

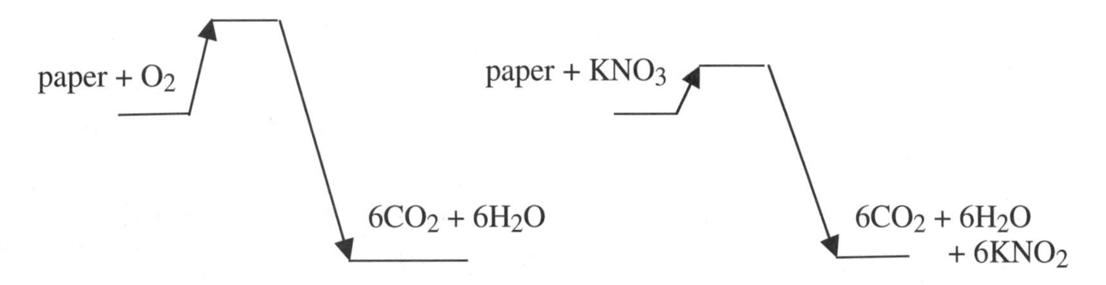

Making sense:
Explain the energy of activation and the heat of reaction in terms of bond breaking and bond making.

If you finish early...
Sketch an energy diagram for the combustion of hydrogen, including the energy of activation. Explain why a spark is needed to ignite a mixture of hydrogen and oxygen.

Making Sense Discussion (15 min)

Major goals: The main goal of this discussion is to make sure students are proficient at interpreting energy diagrams and activation energies. They should be able to examine diagrams and relate them to the heat of reaction and the heat required to get the reaction started. Help students to recognize that the energy of activation has to do with the energy required to break bonds. The heat of reaction is the difference between the energy required to break bonds and the energy released in making bonds.

7. Discuss energy of activation.

You may wish to ask students to draw graphs on the board showing different types of reactions that you describe.

Discussion goals:
Discuss why energy is needed to start an exothermic reaction.

Sample questions:

How can you determine the energy of activation from an energy diagram?

Why is a spark needed to start a combustion reaction?

Why did the paper in the "Writing with Fire" demonstration react with potassium nitrate but not with oxygen?

What do you need to do to get the paper to react with oxygen in the air? (Can you use a match that has been blown out?)

Is the energy of activation for the reverse reaction of combustion larger or smaller? Explain.

Points to cover:

It takes energy to get a fire started. This is easy to see if you have ever tried to start a fire by rubbing two sticks together. Most of the time when we light a fire we do not have to work so hard. We simply pull out a lighter or a match and the match does the work for us to start the barbecue or the presto log.

Most chemical reactions (not just combustion reactions) require some sort of energy input to get them started. This is called the **activation energy.** The match that lights a fire is responsible for delivering the activation energy that gets the chemical reaction of combustion going. Most chemical reactions have some sort of activation energy. In other words, most reactions begin with a push of some sort.

The activation energy shows up on an energy diagram as a small barrier that must be overcome before a reaction goes forward. This "speed bump" or barrier is simply the energy needed to start the reaction. You can see that when the speed bump on an energy diagram is small, the activation energy is low, and that reaction is easier to get started.

8. Discuss bond breaking and bond making.

Have two bar magnets on hand to use in demonstrating bond breaking and bond making between two atoms. The magnets can be labeled with atoms if you wish, such as O and O.

Discussion goals:

Assist students in relating energy changes to what is happening on a particulate level during a reaction.

Sample questions:

Does bond breaking require or release energy? Explain.

Does bond making require or release energy? Explain.

Just because a reaction is endothermic, does that mean there is only bond breaking occurring during that reaction? Explain.

Just because a reaction is exothermic, does that mean there is only bond making occurring during that reaction? Explain.

How is the heat of reaction related to bond breaking and bond making?

If more heat is required to break bonds than is released for making bonds, is heat absorbed or released? Explain.

Points to cover:
The first step of most chemical reactions is the breaking of some of the existing bonds. The energy that is needed to initiate or start this chemical process is called the activation energy. Just like breaking anything, it takes a certain amount of effort or work to break a bond. Thus, **bond breaking** requires an input of energy into a system. This is because atoms are held together by attractive forces. These attractive forces must be overcome if a bond is going to be broken. (Demonstrate how it takes effort and energy to pull the bar magnets apart because of their attractive forces. Or, challenge one or two of the students to pull them apart.)

Bond making, on the other hand, releases a certain amount of energy. This concept is a bit harder to grasp, but the bar magnets can help us to picture bond making. If two magnets are brought close to each other so that the attractive ends are anywhere near each other, they will quickly snap together. This is like the energy that is released when atoms come together through attraction. It doesn't take any effort on our part to bring the magnets together. In fact, the magnets help to pull our hands together; it would be an effort to keep them from coming together.

Equal and opposite processes must have equal and opposite energy transfer, as indicated by the law of conservation of energy. Thus, if energy is required to break a bond, the same amount of energy is released when the same bond forms.

Bond energy: The energy required to break a bond. Bond breaking is endothermic. Bond making is exothermic.

9. Discuss rates of reactions.

Discussion goals:
Assist students in considering how the speed of a reaction is related to the activation energy.

Sample questions:
What factors influence the speed at which a reaction proceeds?
How does surface area affect the reaction rate?
How does mixing affect the reaction rate?
How does the energy of activation affect the reaction rate?

Points to cover:
Some reactions are over in a flash, while others proceed at a snail's pace. The rusting of an iron bridge is a very slow reaction. The combustion of a balloon full of methane gas is a very rapid reaction. Several factors affect the rate at which a reaction will proceed. One factor affecting **reaction rate** is temperature. When the temperature is raised this means the average kinetic energy of the reactant particles is also raised. The particles move more rapidly and more collisions between particles are possible. When more collisions are possible, the probability of atoms rearranging increases.

As we learned in previous classes, the size of the reactants can also affect the rate of a reaction. In combustion reactions, smaller sized fuels, like sawdust or twigs, burn more rapidly than large fuels, like an entire tree or a wooden table. The size of the fuel affects the mixing of the reactants. Thus, the degree of mixing of the reactants is also related to the rate of a reaction. A balloon containing a mixture of hydrogen and oxygen gases will combust much more explosively and rapidly than a balloon containing just hydrogen gas. Reactants that are mixed well will react more rapidly. This is why stirring increases the rate of a reaction.

In general, the activation energy can give us a clue about the rate of a reaction. Reactions with very high activation energies proceed slowly. Reactions with low activation energies proceed more rapidly.

A **catalyst** is a substance that lowers the activation energy of a reaction. A catalyst changes the rate at which a reaction occurs. The catalyst is neither consumed, nor changed by the reaction. An energy diagram showing the effect of a catalyst on the energetics of the reaction would look something like the following.

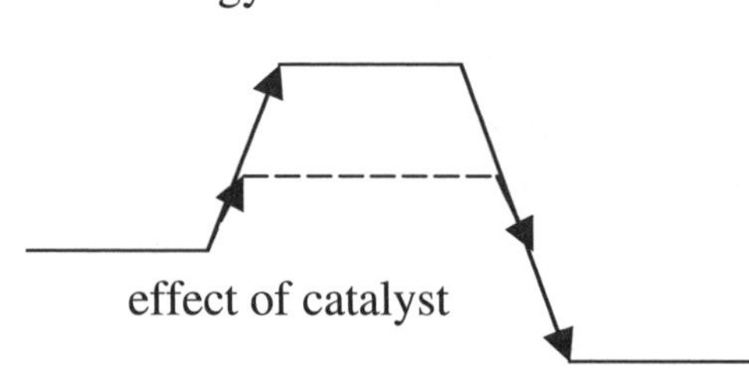

Reaction rate: The speed at which a reaction proceeds. The reaction rate is effected by temperature, mixing, and surface area. Reactions with high activation energies proceed slowly.

Catalyst: A substance that lowers the activation energy for a reaction. A catalyst is not consumed by the reaction.

Check-in (5 min)

10. Introduce the Check-in exercise.

Write the following exercise on the board for students to complete individually.

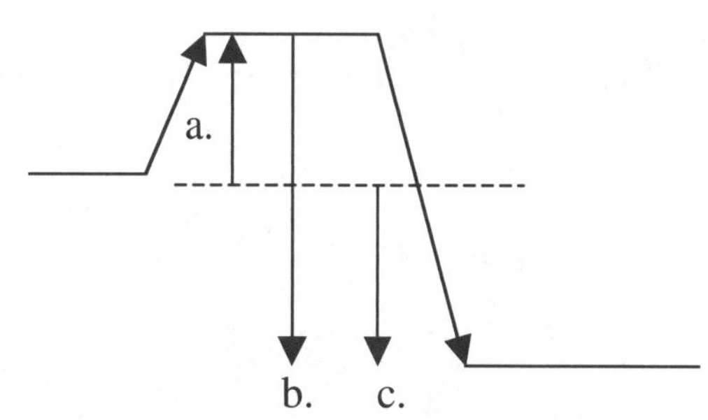

Use the energy diagram to answer the questions.

- Which arrow represents the activation energy – heat going into system?
- Which arrow represents the heat of reaction – net energy released by the reaction?
- For the reaction described by the energy diagram, is the energy required to break bonds greater than the energy released upon forming bonds? Explain.

11. Discuss the Check-in exercise.

Get a sense of the level of understanding by taking a vote, collecting students' work, or asking students to defend their choices.

Discussion goals:
Make sure students understand how to interpret energy diagrams.

Sample questions:
Why is heat required to start the reaction?
Is the reaction exothermic or endothermic?
Are bonds being broken? Explain.
Are bonds being formed? Explain.
For the reaction, is the energy required to break bonds greater or less than the energy released upon forming bonds?

12. Wrap-up

Assist the students in summarizing what was learned in the class.

- The energy of activation for a chemical reaction is the energy that is required to get a reaction started.
- Breaking bonds requires energy. Making bonds releases energy.
- Energy is required to start a reaction because bonds need to be broken as a first step.
- The heat of reaction is the difference between the energy required to break bonds and the energy released in forming bonds.

Homework

13. Assign homework.

Use the homework provided with the curriculum or assign your own.

Homework – Investigation III – Lesson 2

Refer to the appropriate diagrams to answer the questions:

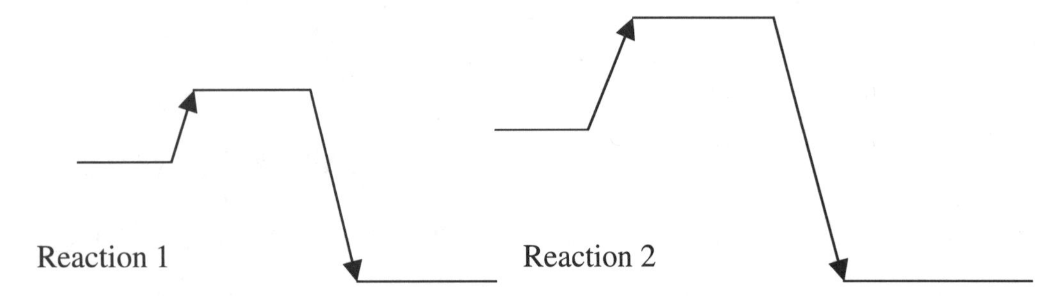

1. Examine the above diagrams. What is similar about Reactions 1 and 2?
2. How are Reactions 1 and 2 different from each other?
3. Draw arrows to show the energy of activation for each reaction. Label them.
4. Draw arrows to show the heat of reaction for each reaction. Label them.
5. Which reaction will take more energy to get started? Explain.
6. Examine the diagram on the right. What does each arrow represent?

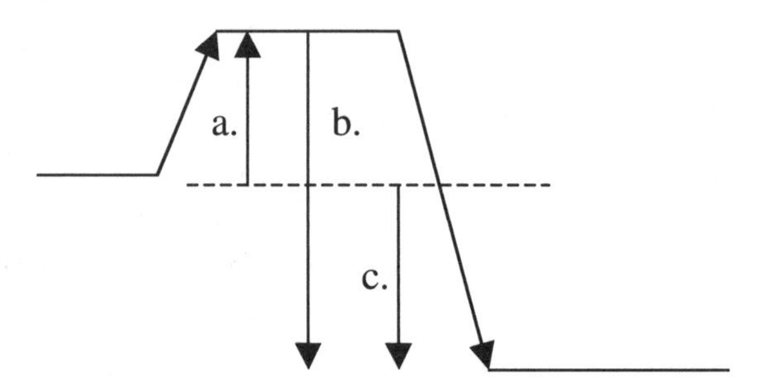

Below is the energy diagram for the reverse reaction of Reaction 2, above.

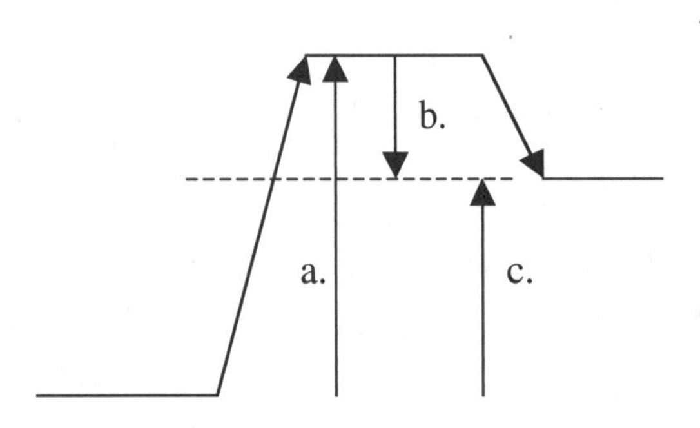

7. Which arrow represents how much energy would be released from the reaction in the form of heat?
8. Which arrow represents the activation energy?
9. Is the activation energy large or small? What does this mean for the reaction?
10. Which arrow represents the heat of reaction? Is it a positive or a negative number? How do you know?
11. Which reaction is more likely to occur, Reaction 2 or its reverse reaction? Explain.

Fire Starter

Name: ____________________

Period: ____ Date: __________

Student Worksheet

Purpose: In this lesson you will have practice interpreting energy diagrams and activation energies.

Answer the following questions.

1. The diagrams below show the changes in energy for two different reactions.

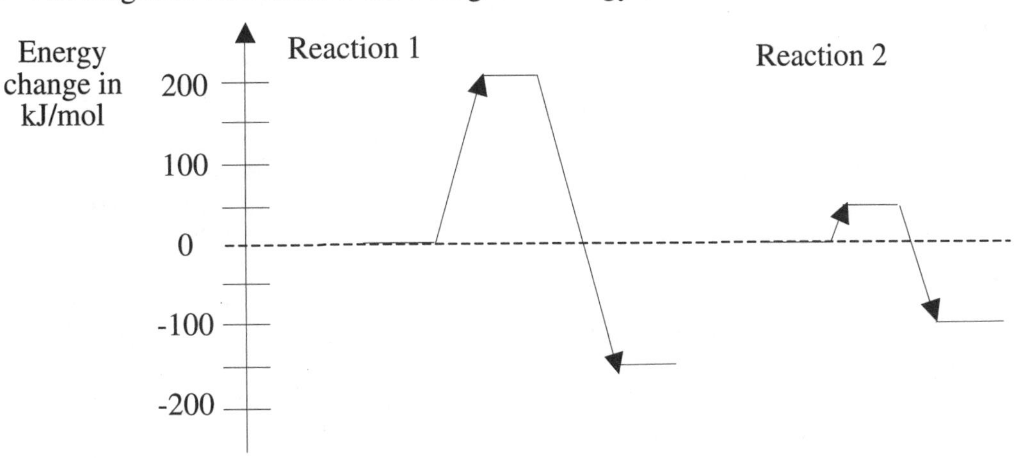

   a. What is the energy of activation for Reaction 1?

   b. What is the energy of activation for Reaction 2?

   c. Which reaction requires more energy to get it started?

   d. What is the heat of reaction for Reaction 1?

   e. What is the heat of reaction for Reaction 2?

   f. Which reaction releases more heat?

2. The diagram below shows one way to think about a chemical reaction. You can think of the top of the hill as the **transition state,** an intermediate step in the reaction. Some bonds of the reactants are broken to reach the transition state. Then, atoms come together to form the bonds in the products.

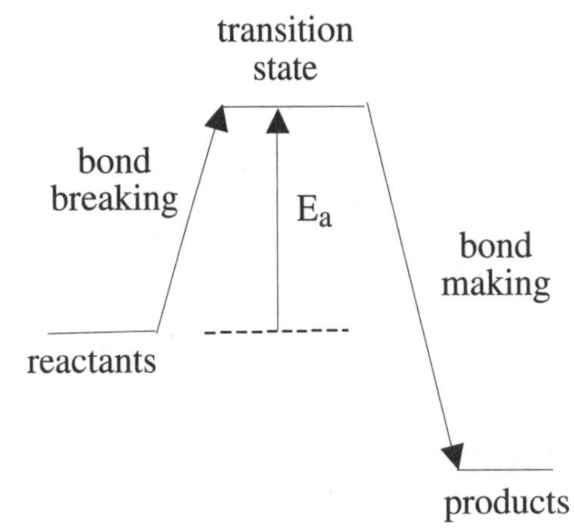

   a. Bond breaking requires energy. How is bond breaking related to the energy of activation E_a? Explain your thinking.

   b. Use the law of conservation of energy to explain why bond making releases energy.

   c. The energy diagram shown represents a combustion reaction. Why is a spark required to get the reaction started?

d. Heat must be supplied to reverse the reverse reaction because the reaction is endothermic. Do you also need more heat to get the reverse reaction started? Explain.

3. The diagram below shows the formation of HCl and HBr.

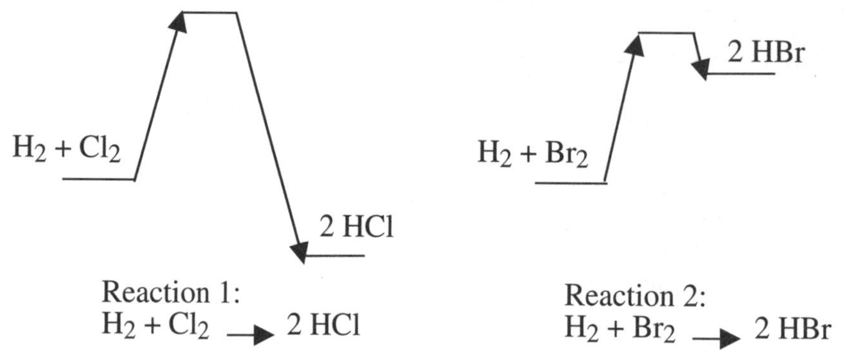

Reaction 1:
$H_2 + Cl_2 \rightarrow 2\ HCl$

Reaction 2:
$H_2 + Br_2 \rightarrow 2\ HBr$

a. Is Reaction 1 exothermic or endothermic?

b. Is Reaction 2 exothermic or endothermic?

c. Which bonds need to be broken to get the reaction started?

d. Which bonds need to be formed?

e. For which reaction is the energy required for bond breaking greater than the energy released for bond making?

4. In the "Writing with Fire" demonstration, the writing was done with the reaction between potassium nitrate (KNO_3) and paper. Use the diagrams below to explain why the paper ignited with KNO_3.

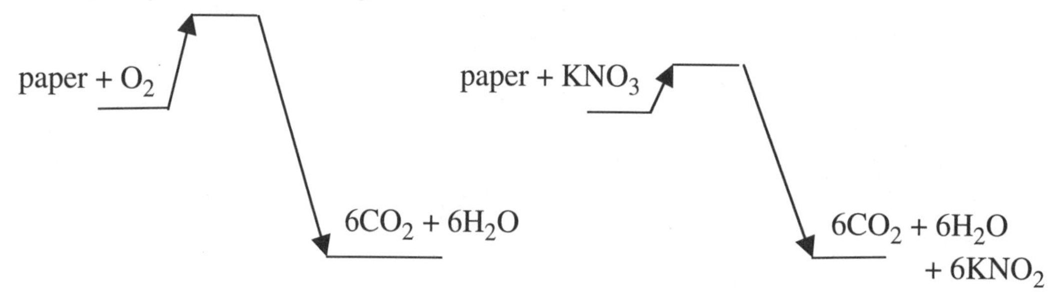

Making sense:
Explain the energy of activation and the heat of reaction in terms of bond breaking and bond making.

If you finish early...
Sketch an energy diagram for the combustion of hydrogen, including the energy of activation. Explain why a spark is needed to ignite a mixture of hydrogen and oxygen.

BEFORE CLASS…

LESSON 3 – Formations

Key Ideas:
The heat of formation of a substance is the energy required to create a mole of the substance from its constituent elements. These elements are always in their standard states (e.g., O_2 instead of O). We can use the heats of formation of the reactants and products to calculate the "energy" of a reaction. $\Delta H_{rxn} = \Delta H_f°(\text{products}) - \Delta H_f°(\text{reactants})$. Chemists prefer to use the term enthalpy when talking about the energy content of a reaction. Enthalpy is similar to heat of reaction except that it takes into account atmospheric pressure and the work that gases do when they are produced or removed by a reaction.

What Takes Place:
Students will complete a worksheet that provides them with practice using the heats of formation of reactants and products to calculate the heats of certain reactions.

Materials:
- Student worksheet

Investigation III – Energy for Change

LESSON 3 – Formations

This lesson introduces the tables of heats of formation, which can be used to determine the heat of a reaction. The term enthalpy is introduced in this lesson, as being more accurate than the term heat of reaction. Enthalpy takes into account changes in pressure due to the presence of gases in either the reactants or the products. The enthalpy of a reaction can be calculated if the enthalpies of the reactants and products are known: $\Delta H_{rxn} = \Delta H(\text{products}) - \Delta H(\text{reactants})$.

Exploring the Topic (5–10 min)

1. Introduce the ChemCatalyst exercise.

Write the following exercise on the board for students to complete individually.

$$H_2\,(g) \;+\; 1/2\,O_2\,(g) \;\rightarrow\; H_2O\,(l) \;+\; 68\text{ kcal}$$

$$H_2\,(g) \;+\; 1/2\,O_2\,(g) \;\rightarrow\; H_2O\,(l) \quad \Delta H \;=\; -68\text{ kcal/mol } H_2O$$

- These two equations seem to contradict each other, but they both refer to the exact same chemical reaction. What does each equation mean?

2. Discuss the ChemCatalyst exercise.

Use the discussion to get a sense of students' initial ideas.

Discussion goals:

Use the students' written responses to stimulate a discussion about heat released versus heat of reaction.

Sample questions:

How would you interpret the two equations?
What does each number represent?
Why is one number negative and the other positive?
How many kcal/mol of energy is released for each mole of water produced?
How many kcal/mol of energy is released for each mole of oxygen used?
Which is lower in energy—the reactants or the products? Explain your thinking.

3. Briefly discuss energy content of reactants and products.

Points to cover:

The first equation in the ChemCatalyst expresses the amount of heat that is released when the reaction proceeds - this value is positive and corresponds to the type of thing we did when we performed calorimetry experiments.

$$H_2\,(g) \;+\; 1/2\,O_2\,(g) \;\rightarrow\; H_2O\,(l) \;+\; 68\text{ kcal}$$

We actively measured the heat that was transferred to a beaker of water by using a thermometer. The beaker of water was the system we were monitoring. **You could say that the focus of this equation is the combustion of hydrogen as a fuel.** Sometimes when heat is released by a reaction, the equation is written as if heat is one of the products. However, this is a bit misleading because the heat is given off to the surroundings, and is no longer a part of the system.

The second equation expresses the energy exchanged between the reaction system and the surroundings.

$$H_2\,(g) \;+\; 1/2\,O_2\,(g) \;\rightarrow\; H_2O\,(l) \quad \Delta H \;=\; -68\text{ kcal/mol }H_2O$$

In this case, heat is released from the system to the surroundings—since the system is losing heat, the value is negative. **You could say that the focus of this particular equation is the formation of liquid water.**

We can also look at a reaction in terms of the energy associated with the reactants and the energy associated with the products. This point of view helps us to see that when a reaction is exothermic, the product molecules are lower in energy than the reactant molecules. When a reaction is endothermic, the product molecules are higher in energy than the reactant molecules. If we know the energies of the reactants and the products, we can use these values to calculate the overall energy of the reaction.

4. Introduce heats of formation.

Points to cover:
Sometimes it takes heat to form a certain product and sometimes heat is released in the formation of a certain product. Whatever this heat is, whether it is positive or negative, it is referred to as the **heat of formation.** Its symbol is $\Delta H_f°$. For example, the heat of formation of one mole of liquid water is –68 kcal.

$$H_2\,(g) \;+\; 1/2\,O_2\,(g) \;\rightarrow\; H_2O\,(l) \quad \Delta H_f \;=\; -68\text{ kcal/mol }H_2O$$

Heats of formation are determined experimentally. Their values are found in tables in the back of some chemistry books. Remember, heats of formation reactions are defined as those in which a substance is formed directly from the most basic elements involved. These elements must be in their standard states. A *standard state* is whatever state an element is found in at standard temperature and pressure. For example, oxygen is found as O_2 at STP, not as O.

Heats of formation are quite useful. We can use the heats of formation to calculate the heat of a reaction, without actually having to perform that experiment. We must simply add together the heats of formation of the reactants, add together the heats of formation of the products, and find the difference between the two. The formula is below:

$$\Delta H_{rxn} = (\text{the sum of } \Delta H_f \text{ products}) - (\text{the sum of } \Delta H_f \text{ reactants})$$

It is extremely important to pay attention to the negative and positive signs when completing these calculations. (Remember, subtracting a negative number is the same as adding that number. Adding two negative numbers together results in a larger negative number.)

5. Explain the purpose of today's activity.

If you wish you can write the main question on the board.

Points to cover:
Tell students they will be considering several reactions and gathering information to answer the question: "How can we calculate the energy of a reaction without measuring it experimentally?"

Activity - Formations (15 min)

6. Introduce the activity. (Worksheet)

Pass out the worksheets. Ask students to work in pairs.

You will use the table to answer the questions below.

Heats of formation:

Substance	Heat of formation ΔH_f°	Substance	Heat of formation ΔH_f°
CO_2 (g)	–394 kJ/mol	C_2H_6 (g)	–85 kJ/mol
C (s)	0	$C_6H_{12}O_2$ (s)	–1273.0 kJ/mol
H_2O (l)	–286 kJ/mol	Fe (s)	0
O_2 (g)	0	Fe (g)	416 kJ/mol
N_2 (g)	0	FeO (s)	–272 kJ/mol
N (g)	473 kJ/mol	Fe_2O_3 (s)	–822 kJ/mol
NO (g)	90 kJ/mol	CaO (s)	–636 kJ/mol
NO_2 (g)	34 kJ/mol	HCl (aq)	–167 kJ/mol
N_2O_4 (g)	9.7 kJ/mol	$CaCO_3$ (s)	–1207 kJ/mol
CH_4 (g)	–75 kJ/mol	MgO (s)	–602 kJ/mol
O (g)	248 kJ/mol	Mg (s)	0

1. The heat of formation of a compound is the energy transferred in order to make the compound from the elements. Notice that the heats of formation of the elements as they are found at 25°C are set equal to zero.

a. What is the heat of formation of ethane (C_2H_6)? (–85 kJ/mol)

b. Write the equation associated with the heat of formation of one mole of calcium oxide. (CaO). ($Ca + 0.5\ O_2 \rightarrow CaO$)

c. When NO_2 is formed from the elements, is heat released required? (required)

d. Give an example of a substance that *requires* heat in order to form it from the elements. (O(g), NO(g), Fe(g), etc.)

e. Why is the heat of formation of gaseous oxygen atoms, O(g), positive? (energy is required to break the O=O bond)

2. You can use tables of heats of formation to predict heats of reactions. The diagram below shows how to use heats of formation to predict the heat of reaction when calcium oxide (CaO) combines with carbon dioxide (CO_2) to form calcium carbonate ($CaCO_3$).

   $CaO\ (s) + CO_2\ (g) \rightarrow CaCO_3\ (s)$

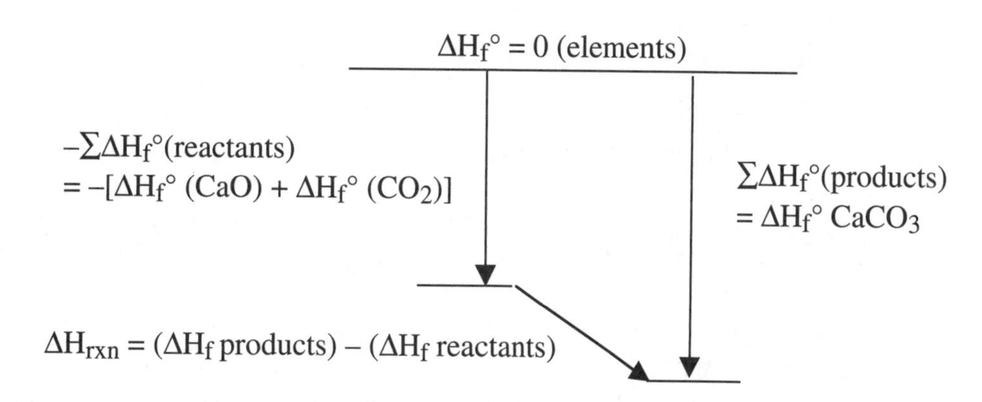

a. What is the heat of formation of CaO? (–636 kJ/mol)

b. What is the heat of formation of CO_2? (–394 kJ/mole)

c. What is the sum of the heats of formation of the reactants, CaO and CO_2? ([– 636 + (–394)] = –1030 kJ/mol)

d. How much energy is released when $CaCO_3$ is formed from its elements? (–1207 kJ/mol)

e. Now insert these values into the equation and solve for the heat of reaction. $\Delta H_{rxn} = (\Delta H_f$ products$) - (\Delta H_f$ reactants$)$ [–1207 – (–1030)] = –1207 + 1030 = –178 kJ/mol)

f. Is the reaction exothermic or endothermic? (exothermic)

3. Notice that the heat of formation is given in kJ/mol. In other words, the heat refers to the formation of 1 mole. How much heat is required to form 2 moles of H_2O? (2 mol (–286 kJ/mol) = –572 kJ)

4. Use the heats of formation to figure out the heat of reaction for the combustion of methane, CH_4.

   a. First, write the equation for the combustion of methane, CH_4. Make sure it is balanced.

   $$CH_4 + 2\,O_2 \rightarrow CO_2 + 2\,H_2O$$

   b. What is the sum of the heats of formation of the reactants? (–75 + 2(0) = –75 kJ/mol)

   c. How much energy is required to form the products from the elements? (Don't forget the coefficients.) (–394 – 2(286) = –966 kJ/mol)

   d. Solve for ΔH_{rxn}. (–966 + 75 = –891 kJ/mol)

   e. What experiment can you do to check your result? How does your calculation compare with the value given in Lesson II-4? (calorimetry, The value given in Lesson II-4 is –213 kcal/mol. To convert to kJ/mol: 4.184(–213) = –891 kJ/mol)

Making sense:
Explain how you use heats of formation to determine the heat of a reaction.

If you finish early...
How many kJ of heat are released when 6.4 grams of propane are burned?

Making Sense Discussion (10–15 min)

Major goals: The point of this discussion is to make sense of the procedure that students went through on their worksheets. Essentially, they followed Hess's Law in calculating the heat of various reactions, by combining the heats of formation of the various components of a reaction. In addition, some clarification of nomenclature should occur here, since the terms heat, energy, and enthalpy are sometimes used to refer to the same (or closely similar) concept.

7. Introduce Hess's Law of Heat Summation.

You may wish to complete a practice heat of reaction problem on the board.

Discussion goals:
Assist students in clarifying what they learned from the worksheet.

Sample questions:
How can you determine the heat of reaction for the combustion of propane?

Points to cover:

The path that a reaction takes is not always as straightforward as it might seem. In fact, there are often many intermediate steps in the creation of products from reactants. However, no matter what route is taken, the net result is the same energetically. A man named G.H. Hess determined this to be true. He is responsible for developing **Hess's Law,** also known as the **Law of Heat Summation.** This law states that the sum of the heats of formation of the various steps of a reaction will be equal to the heat of the overall reaction. Thus we can use the heats of formation of the reactants and products to determine the overall heat of a reaction.

Recall that the heat of formation of a substance is the energy required to create a mole of the substance from its constituent elements in their standard states. This means that we must measure the energy it takes to form each substance from the most basic substances on the planet. Once chemists have these values, they are collected in a table for easy reference. You may have noticed on your worksheet that the heat of formation of the elements in their standard states is zero. They already exist in nature, so it does not require any energy exchange to form them. Examples of elemental substances are Fe(s), Mg(s), O_2, H_2, N_2, C(s) and so on.

Hess's Law was a great breakthrough because it meant that the energy changes of a reaction could be determined without having to perform careful calorimetry experiments. However, if we know the heats of formation we can determine the heat of the overall reaction.

Sample problem:

Calculate the heat of reaction for the reaction of NO_2 with itself to form N_2O_4

$$2\,NO_2 \rightarrow N_2O_4$$

$$\Delta H_{rxn} = (\Delta H_f^\circ \text{ products}) - (\Delta H_f^\circ \text{ reactants})$$

$$\Delta H_{rxn} = (\Delta H_f^\circ\ N_2O_4) - 2\Delta H_f^\circ\ (NO_2)$$

Now solve for $\Delta H_f^\circ rxn$:

$$\text{heat of reaction} = (+9.7 \text{ kJ/mol}) - 2(34 \text{ kJ/mol})$$

$$= (9.7 \text{ kJ/mol}) - (68 \text{ kJ/mol})$$

$$= -58 \text{ kJ/mol}$$

8. Clarify thermochemistry terms.

Write these terms on the board where needed.

Points to cover:

When talking about thermochemistry, a lot of terms are used interchangeably. However, each term has a specific meaning. So far we have used the term heat of reaction to mean the overall energy input or output of a reaction. A more accurate measurement of the energy exchanged during a reaction is the **enthalpy of reaction.** Enthalpy is simply the energy of the reaction adjusted to take into account atmospheric pressure. This is because some of the energy coming from a reaction can be due to pressure changes caused by the expansion or shrinking of gases that are involved. Just think of the energy that would be expressed if a tanker full of gasoline ignited. The rapidly expanding gases would cause a huge explosion. For our purposes, from now on we will assume that all calculations have been made at constant pressure. In this case the change in enthalpy is equal to the heat of reaction.

Heat of reaction – energy input or output of a reaction
Molar heat of reaction – energy input or output of a reaction per mole of reactant (or product) used
Enthalpy – the heat (or energy) content of a system at constant pressure
Heat of formation - the heat released or required (the change in enthalpy) during the formation of a pure substance from its elements.

The enthalpy of any reaction can be written as the sum of the enthalpies of formation of the products minus the sum of the enthalpies of formation of the reactants. $\Delta H_{rxn} = \Sigma\ \Delta H(\text{products}) - \Sigma\Delta H(\text{reactants})$

If you become confused by any of these terms just know that the words "heat," "energy," and "enthalpy" are often used interchangeably here. Replacing one term with another may assist you in comprehending what is being said. For instance, if a problem asks for the enthalpy of reaction, remember what you learned about calculating the heat of reaction.

Check-in (5 min)

9. Introduce the Check-in exercise.

Write the following exercise on the board for students to complete individually.

- Explain how you can you calculate the heat of reaction (or the enthalpy of reaction) for the following reaction, from the heats of formation of the reactants and products.

$$2Mg\ (s) + O_2\ (g) \rightarrow 2\ MgO\ (s)$$

- Write out the formula for this calculation, using the compounds in the above reaction.

10. Discuss the Check-in exercise.

Get a sense of the level of understanding by taking a vote, collecting students' work, or asking students to defend their choices.

Discussion goals:

Make sure students understand how to use the concept of heat of formation.

Sample questions:

How do you use heats of formation to determine the ΔH_{rxn} for the above equation?

Substitute the compounds into the appropriate places in the formula.

What is the $\Delta H_f°$ for $O_2(g)$? Explain.

What is the $\Delta H_f°$ for Mg(s)? Explain.

The heat of reaction for one mole of product is identical to the heat of formation for MgO in this case. Explain why this is true.

Is this reaction exothermic or endothermic?

Answer: ΔH_{rxn} = the sum of the heats of formation of the products minus the sum of the heats of formation of the reactants.

$$\Delta H_{rxn} = 2(\Delta H_f° \text{ MgO}) - [2\ \Delta H_f° (\text{Mg(s)}) + \Delta H_f° (O_2(g))]$$

Students could actually work this one out because they have the ΔH_f values in the table. $\Delta H_{rxn} = 2\ (-601.8 \text{ kJ/mol}) - (0) = -1203.6 \text{ kJ}$ or -601.8 kJ/mol

11. Wrap-up

Assist the students in summarizing what was learned in the class.

- The heat of formation of a substance is the energy required to create a mole of the substance from its constituent elements in their standard states.
- We can calculate the "energy" of a reaction by measuring the difference in energy between the reactants and products. $\Delta H = \Delta H(\text{products}) - \Delta H(\text{reactants})$.
- Enthalpy is a more accurate value to use when talking about the energy content of a reaction.
- Enthalpy is similar to heat of reaction except that it takes into account atmospheric pressure and the work that gases do when they are produced or removed by a reaction.

Homework

12. Assign homework.

Use the homework provided with the curriculum or assign your own.

Homework – Investigation III – Lesson 3

Use the heat of formation table when needed to answer the following questions:

1. What is the heat of formation of iron oxide, $F_2O_3(s)$.?What does this value mean? Why is it negative?
2. What is the heat of formation of nitrogen dioxide, NO_2? Why is this value positive?
3. Why are some of the values in the table equal to zero?
4. Figure out the heat of the following reaction, ΔH_{rxn}. Is it exothermic or endothermic?

$$NO_2 + NO_2 \rightarrow N_2O_4$$

5. The heat of formation of C_2H_4 (g) is +52.5 kJ/mol. The heat of formation of C_2H_6(g) is –85 kJ/mol. What is different about the structures of these two compounds? What do you think makes the heat of formation of one of them negative, and the other positive?
6. The heat of formation of liquid water is –285.8 kJ/mol. The heat of formation of water vapor is –242.0 kJ/mol. Write the equation for this physical change and explain why the values are different.
7. Calculate the heat of the combustion reaction for propane, C_3H_8. First write and balance the equation. The heat of formation of propane is –103.8 kJ/mol. (Remember, you are forming gaseous water vapor as one of the products.)
8. Most heats of formation are negative quantities. What can you conclude from this?

Formations

Name: ______________________

Period: ____ Date: ___________

Student Worksheet

Purpose: This lesson provides you with practice calculating heats of reaction using heats of formation values.

Heats of formation:

Substance	Heat of formation $\Delta H_f°$	Substance	Heat of formation $\Delta H_f°$
CO_2 (g)	–394 kJ/mol	C_2H_6 (g)	–85 kJ/mol
C (s)	0	$C_6H_{12}O_2$ (s)	–1273.0 kJ/mol
H_2O (l)	–286 kJ/mol	Fe (s)	0
O_2 (g)	0	Fe (g)	416 kJ/mol
N_2 (g)	0	FeO (s)	–272 kJ/mol
N (g)	473 kJ/mol	Fe_2O_3 (s)	–822 kJ/mol
NO (g)	90 kJ/mol	CaO (s)	–636 kJ/mol
NO_2 (g)	34 kJ/mol	HCl (aq)	–167 kJ/mol
N_2O_4 (g)	9.7 kJ/mol	$CaCO_3$ (s)	–1207 kJ/mol
CH_4 (g)	–75 kJ/mol	MgO (s)	–602 kJ/mol
O (g)	248 kJ/mol	Mg (s)	0

1. The heat of formation of a compound is the energy transferred in order to make the compound from the elements. Notice that the heats of formation of the elements as they are found at 25°C are set equal to zero.

   a. What is the heat of formation of ethane (C_2H_6)?

   b. Write the equation associated with the heat of formation of one mole of calcium oxide. (CaO).

   c. When NO_2 is formed from the elements, is heat released or required?

   d. Give an example of a substance that *requires* heat in order to form it from the elements.

   e. Why is the heat of formation of gaseous oxygen atoms, O (g), positive?

2. You can use tables of heats of formation to predict heats of reactions. The diagram below shows how to use heats of formation to predict the heat of reaction when calcium oxide (CaO) combines with carbon dioxide (CO_2) to form calcium carbonate ($CaCO_3$).

$$CaO\ (s) \ + \ CO_2\ (g) \ \rightarrow \ CaCO_3\ (s)$$

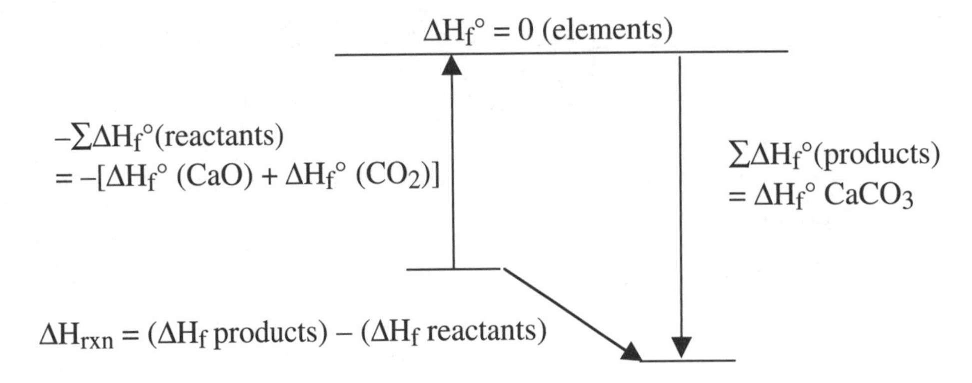

a. What is the heat of formation of CaO?

b. What is the heat of formation of CO_2?

c. What is the sum of the heats of formation of the reactants, CaO and CO_2?

d. How much energy is released when $CaCO_3$ is formed from its elements?

e. Now insert these values into the equation and solve for the heat of reaction.

$$\Delta H_{rxn} = (\Delta H_f \text{ products}) - (\Delta H_f \text{ reactants})$$

f. Is the reaction exothermic or endothermic?

3. Notice that the heat of formation is given in kJ/mol. In other words, the heat refers to the formation of 1 mole. How much heat is required to form 2 moles of H_2O?

4. Use the heats of formation to figure out the heat of reaction for the combustion of methane, CH_4.
   a. First, write the equation for the combustion of methane, CH_4. Make sure it is balanced.

   b. What is the sum of the heats of formation of the reactants?

   c. How much energy is required to form the products from the elements? (Don't forget the coefficients.)

   d. Solve for ΔH_{rxn}.

   e. What experiment can you do to check your result? How does your calculation compare with the value given in Lesson II-4?

Making sense:
Explain how you use heats of formation to determine the heat of a reaction.

If you finish early...
How many kJ of heat are released when 6.4 grams of propane are burned?

BEFORE CLASS…

LESSON 4 – Ashes to Ashes

Key Ideas:
This activity serves to summarize the thermochemistry learned over the course of the *Fire* unit. The emphasis is on three main areas—the nature of heat, combustion, and energy exchanges during chemical change.

What Takes Place:
Students complete a worksheet that allows them to review what they've learned in the *Fire* unit. The concept map for fire is posted and brought up to date with any new information.

Materials:
- Student worksheet
- Fire Concept Map

Investigation III – Energy for Change

LESSON 4 – Ashes to Ashes

This lesson wraps up the *Fire* unit. It provides students with practice applying the concepts they have learned throughout these investigations. Students complete a worksheet that covers the material that was presented during the unit. In addition, the Fire Concept Map helps to organize and summarize the remaining concepts that were introduced.

Exploring the Topic (5–10 min)

1. Introduce the ChemCatalyst exercise.

Write the following exercise on the board for students to complete individually.

- Many reactions are easily reversible. However, when a tree burns down, it is essentially impossible to recover the tree by reversing the combustion reaction. Examine the two chemical equations and explain why only one is easily reversible.

$$2\,NO_2 \rightarrow N_2O_4 \qquad \Delta H = 9.7\text{ kJ/mol}$$

$$2\,C_8H_{18} + 25\,O_2 \rightarrow 16\,CO_2 + 18\,H_2O \qquad \Delta H = -5439\text{ kJ/mol}$$

2. Discuss the ChemCatalyst exercise.

Use the discussion to get a sense of students' initial ideas.

Discussion goals:

Use the students' written responses to stimulate a discussion about.

Sample questions:

What makes one reaction easily reversible?

Can you make any generalizations about the activation energies for these two reactions?

What does it take to get these two reactions to go forward?

What does it take to get these two reactions to reverse?

How are these two chemical reactions similar?

How are these two chemical reactions different?

What does the enthalpy of reaction have to do with the reversibility of the reaction?

3. Explain the purpose of today's activity.

If you wish you can write the main question on the board.

Points to cover:

Tell students they will be gathering information to answer the question: "What concepts were introduced during the *Fire* unit?"

Activity – Ashes to Ashes (15 min)

4. Introduce the activity. (Worksheet)

Pass out the worksheet. Ask students to work on it individually.

Answer the following questions:

1. When sodium chloride is dissolved in a beaker containing 100 mL water, the temperature of the water decreases by several degrees. Draw this beaker in the box at the right and use arrows to show the direction of heat transfer.
2. The temperature of the solution of sodium chloride and water has decreased by 4.5 degrees Celsius. How many calories of heat were transferred during the dissolving? Show your work. (calories = ΔT x specific heat of water x grams of water, 4.5 x 1.0 x 100 = 450 calories)
3. How many calories of heat are required to do the following?
   a. Raise the temperature of 50 grams of water from 25˚C to boiling. (75˚ x 1 x 50 = 3,750 calories)
   b. Raise the temperature of 100 grams of water from 25˚C to boiling. (7500 calories)
4. What is the formal definition of a calorie? (the amount of heat it takes to raise the temperature of one gram of water by 1˚C)
5. What kind of information does a calorie tell us? When I say that the calorie content of a Cheeto® is 200 kilocalories, what does this mean?
6. Write and balance the reaction for the combustion of pentanol, $C_5H_{12}O$.
   ($C_5H_{12}O + 5\,O_2 \rightarrow 5\,CO_2 + 6\,H_2O$)

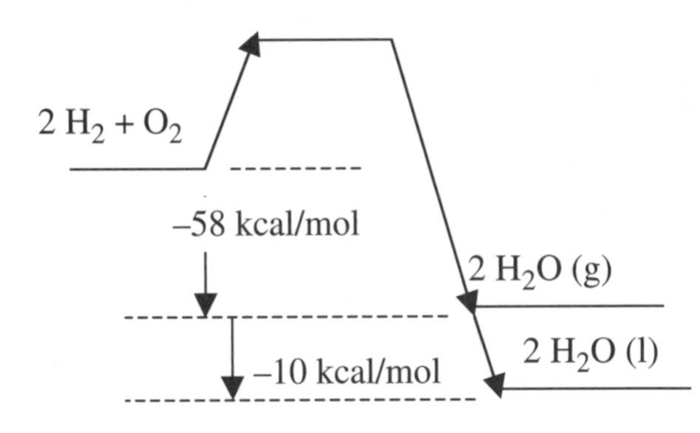

7. List at least six pieces of information that you can get from this energy diagram.
   What is the ΔH for the formation of liquid water?
   (–68 kcal/mol)
8. What is the ΔH for the formation of hydrogen and oxygen gases from water vapor? (+58 kcal/mol)

9. Write the forward and the reverse reaction for this particular diagram. Draw and label the energy diagram associated with the formation of hydrogen and oxygen from liquid water, in the box at right.

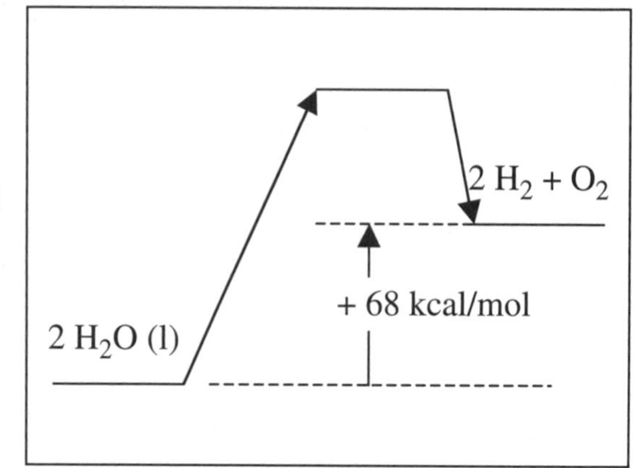

10. How many kcal of heat would be released if 20 moles of liquid water is produced in the forward reaction? How many kJ is this? (680 kcal, 2845 kJ)
11. How many kcal of energy are required to produce the following? How many kJ? (Hint: write out the chemical equation, solving for one mole of water)
    a. 1/2 mole of oxygen gas from water vapor (58 kcal, 243 kJ)
    b. 2 moles of oxygen gas from liquid water (272 kcal, 1138 kJ)
    c. 32 grams of oxygen gas from liquid water (136 kcal, 569 kJ)
12. Label the activation energy on both your diagrams. What does the activation energy tell you about these particular reactions? (The activation energy tells us that this
13. In energy terms, why are some reactions easily reversible while others are not?
14. Explain what the law of conservation of energy means.

Making sense:
What information would you need to tell if a chemical reaction might result in a fire?

If you finish early...
Imagine you burn 10 grams of butane. The ΔH for butane is –147.6 kJ/mol. How much energy will be released by the combustion of these 10 grams of butane?

Making Sense Discussion (10–15 min)

Major goals: The main goal of this discussion is to complete a quick review of the various terms and concepts introduced in the *Fire* unit. You may wish to complete some worked examples on the board for students. Or, you may wish to simply go over the worksheet problems as a class. Leave time to update and summarize the Fire Concept Map.

5. Discuss the problems on the worksheet.

You may wish to ask students to complete equations and diagrams on the board in front of the class.

Discussion goals:
Assist students in recalling the various terms and concepts that were introduced in this unit.

6. Summarize the concepts learned in the *Fire* unit.

Quickly review the concepts and terms covered in the *Fire* unit. You may wish to create a list of the main topics and terms on the board as a study guide.

Discussion goals:

Assist students in recalling the various terms and concepts that were introduced in this unit.

Sample questions:

What do energy exchanges have to do with changes in matter?
Describe what is going on when a reaction in a beaker feels cold to the touch.
What is thermal equilibrium?
Do energy exchanges occur during physical changes? Explain.
Why is it important to define the system and the surroundings in an experiment?
If you are doing a calorimetry experiment, what constitutes “the system”?
What things do we keep track of going into and out of a system?
What is a calorie? What do calories keep track of?
What types of substances make good fuels? Bad fuels?
What conditions are necessary for combustion to take place?
What kinds of reactions produce a flame?
What is latent heat?
What is an explosion?
How can you tell, by looking at a chemical equation, whether it will result in a fire?
Describe what the activation energy of a reaction is.
Why do exothermic reactions have a negative value for heat of reaction?
Name one endothermic reaction.
Describe what heat is.
Which makes a better fuel, a molecule with a large carbon chain or one with a short one? Explain.
Why do trees and fossil fuels take so long to create?
What does the law of conservation of energy tell us?

7. Use the Fire Map to summarize the *Fire* unit.

Post the Fire Concept Map in the room. Add any concepts that have not yet been summarized on the map.

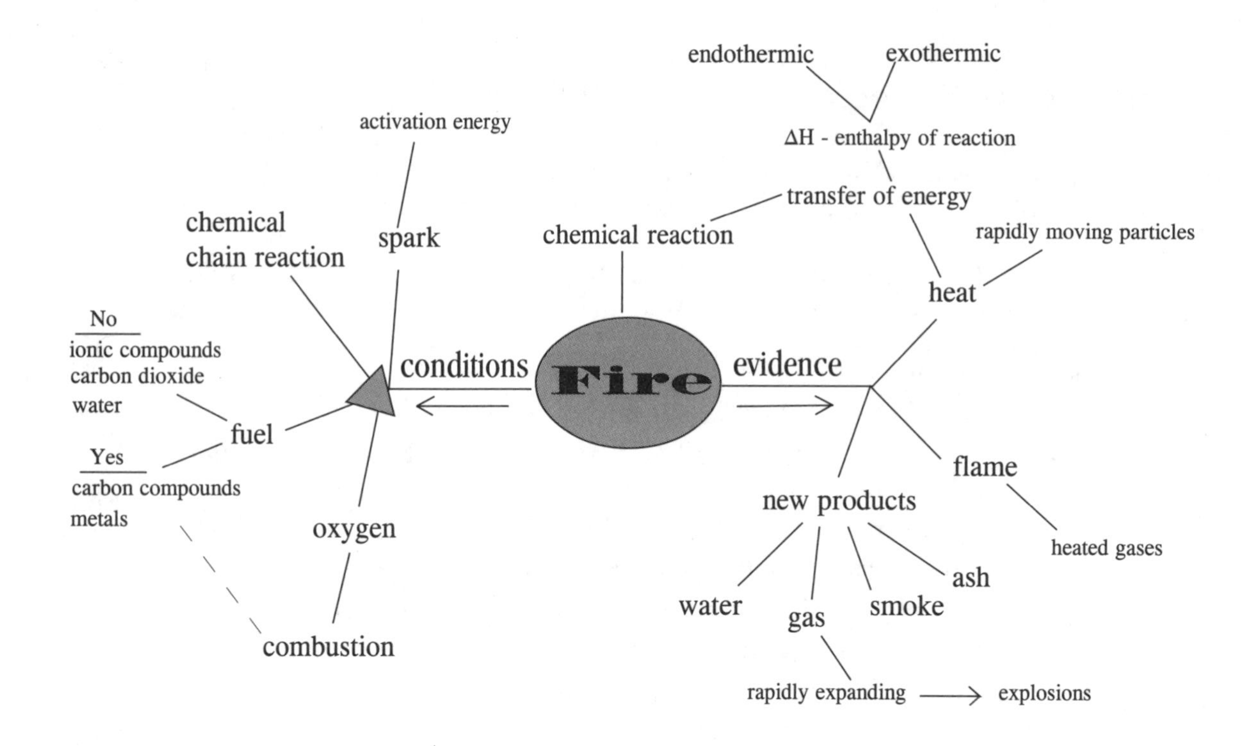

Check-in (5 min)

8. No Check-in for this class.

9. Wrap-up

No wrap-up necessary for this class.

Homework

10. Assign homework.

Use the homework provided with the curriculum or assign your own.

Homework – Investigation III – Lesson 4

1. Review what you have learned in the *Fire* unit in preparation for a unit test.
2. Use your concept map to create statements about the concepts you have learned in this unit. Two examples are given below. Create at least ten more summary sentences.

   Examples: Fire is the result of a chemical reaction.
   Oxygen is required for combustion to occur.

Ashes to Ashes

Name: ______________________

Period: ____ Date: ___________

Purpose: This lesson provides you with practice problems that will allow you to review the concepts you've learned in this unit.

Answer the following questions:

1. When sodium chloride is dissolved in a beaker containing 100 mL of water, the temperature of the water decreases by several degrees. Draw this beaker in the box at the right and use arrows to show the direction of heat transfer.

2. The temperature of the solution of sodium chloride and water has decreased by 4.5 degrees Celsius. How many calories of heat were transferred during the dissolving? Show your work.

3. How many calories of heat are required to do the following?
   a. Raise the temperature of 50 grams of water from 25˚C to boiling.

   b. Raise the temperature of 100 grams of water from 25˚C to boiling.

4. What is the formal definition of a calorie?

5. What kind of information does a calorie tell us? When I say that the calorie content of a Cheeto® is 200 kilocalories, what does this mean?

6. Write and balance the reaction for the combustion of pentanol, $C_5H_{12}O$.

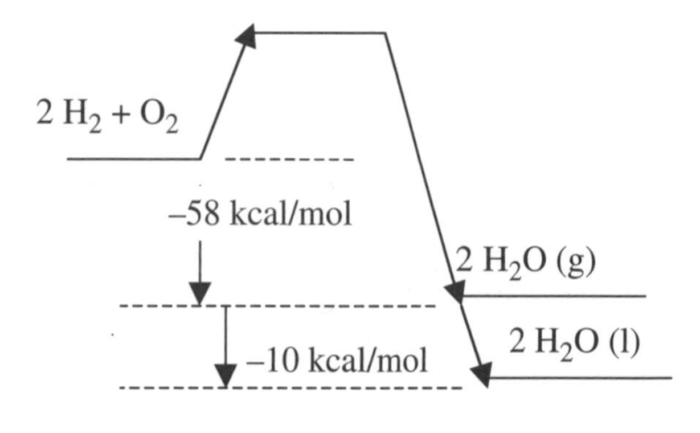

7. List at least six pieces of information that you can get from this energy diagram.

8. What is the ΔH for the formation of liquid water?

9. What is the ΔH for the formation of hydrogen and oxygen gases from water vapor?

10. Write the forward and the reverse reaction for this particular diagram.

11. Draw and label the energy diagram associated with the formation of hydrogen and oxygen from liquid water, in the box at right.

12. How many kcal of heat would be released if 20 moles of liquid water were produced in this reaction? How many kJoules is this?

13. How many kcal of energy are required to produce the following? How many kJoules?
    a. 1/2 mole of oxygen gas from water vapor
    b. 2 moles of oxygen gas from liquid water
    c. 32 grams of oxygen gas from liquid water

14. Label the activation energy on both your diagrams. What does the activation energy tell you about these particular reactions?

15. In energy terms, why are some reactions easily reversible while others are not?

16. Explain what the law of conservation of energy means.

Making sense:
What information would you need to tell if a chemical reaction might result in a fire?

If you finish early...
Imagine you burn 10 grams of butane. The ΔH for butane is –147.6 kJ/mol. How much energy will be released by the combustion of these 10 grams of butane?